Footprints in the Sea –
Tales of a Marine Biologist

———— ∞ ————

———— ∞ ————

Viv Gotto

BALLYHAY BOOKS

Published by Ballyhay Books,
an imprint of Laurel Cottage Ltd.
Donaghadee, N. Ireland 2004.
Printed by CLE Ltd..

ISBN 1 900935 38 4

---------------- ∞ ----------------

Foreword

---------------- ∞ ----------------

"I trust, Viv, you've no objection to your name being given to a small, obese, legless parasite." With these words a biological colleague recently christened a tiny newly discovered crustacean collected off the Fife coast and *Sphaeronella gottoi* was unveiled to the scientific world. I had no objection whatsoever. The pleasant little compliment of having your name given to a new species is, I suppose, rather like being made a godparent – but without the subsequent responsibility. It's one of the things that help to make your choice of a biological career seem worthwhile.

Since my life has never struck me as unusually noteworthy, the nine chapters that follow were not intended to be autobiographical in any strict sense. Over the past forty years I have simply jotted down incidents for no better reason than that they have remained fresh in my memory. However, several friends, on hearing the occasional story, suggested that I should commit it more formally to paper. Having done this and used a few tolerant acquaintances as guinea pigs, it became apparent that they wished for wider information on my own background. I therefore felt impelled to provide at least the following synopsis.

I was born on 13th September, 1921 – a few weeks after Northern Ireland had become a separate entity within the United Kingdom. We lived in south Belfast and the house where I was born is still standing, despite very recent attempts to demolish it. Its continued existence is not, I assure you, in any way connected with myself, but merely because it happens to be listed as a standard example of 1870s Victoriana. I was the youngest child, preceded by a brother ten years older and two sisters. Our parents were also born in Belfast within a half-mile radius. Dad was the eighth child in a family of nine and my mother, three years older, was the second of seven. Both happened to be Protestants and I imagine that the large families resulted from an awareness of

J.P. Corry

child mortality at that period of the nineteenth century.

Dad's father reached Northern Ireland after spending his early years in Schleswig-Holstein on the German-Danish border, although the Gotto family had probably originated much further south in the neighbourhood of Genoa. He met and married Margaret Corry, daughter of James P. Corry who became a Member of Parliament for South Belfast and head of a rapidly expanding timber firm. At Westminster he was highly regarded by Benjamin Disraeli, then Prime Minister, who selected him to second the Address to Queen Victoria at the opening of Parliament in 1880.

The Corrys were a rather unusual family, the males tending to develop highly macho personalities. James' younger brother William was endowed with considerable strength, which he evidently enjoyed demonstrating. No pack of cards could withstand his powerful grip, being shredded in twain with casual ease. But his tour de force was even more spectacular. To entertain his family and friends, he would scale the long staircase of his home in South Belfast, standing on his hands and with a 56 pound weight dangling from his teeth.

Although two of my father's older brothers entered the Corry family firm, Dad created a successful small business in the linen industry. My mother's family name, Pinion, was of Huguenot extraction, with an Ulster base in Waringstown. Her father, James, had managed the Cheshire Lines Railway Company before moving to Belfast as head of the Belfast and County Down Railway. He died comparatively young, never fully recovering from a blow to the head by a bottle-wielding hooligan at Downpatrick station.

My Scottish granny, however, lived to the age of ninety, scarcely ever leaving her home in Belfast's Lower Crescent.

My brother Arthur and sisters Merrill and Priscilla finished their education in English boarding schools. I was destined for this same rather barbarous fate until, after a year at a preparatory school, I fell victim to a mysterious viral infection which lasted for four years and effectively sabotaged any formal attempts at education. I was eventually rescued from total ignorance by the combined efforts of an academically brilliant family who coached youngsters like myself. The husband, a classicist, took care of English, Latin and History. His wife, a fine mathematician, removed my long-standing terror of numbers and their daughter (not much older than myself and the fleeting object of a hopeless teenage passion) taught me French. Thanks to them, I passed the Queen's matriculation exam at the age of eighteen.

Zoology was to be my main subject. I cannot remember a time when I was not fascinated by the natural world. At the age of eleven, I was proposed by the distinguished, old Ulster photographer, Robert Welch, for membership of the Belfast Naturalists' Field Club. It was in the Zoology Department where I first met Gwyneth in that surreal autumn of 1940 when invasion by Nazi Germany seemed extremely probable. Her Welsh father, James Jones, was Chief Engineer to the Ministry of Finance in Northern Ireland and, as such, organised the drainage of the Bann River basin. He was an ingenious inventor, having contributed significantly to the early attempts to launch aircraft from ships and had also designed an automatic cover for the centre court at Wimbledon. Unlike me, Gwyneth had a highly impressive school record allied to a fair degree of all-round athletic ability. Although we are almost exactly the same age, she was a year ahead of me in our university courses.

The rest, as they say, is history – or if not history, at least a few slices of experience from my own life in a dramatically uncertain period. I am very aware that the two chapters dealing with my researches into the private lives of tiny crustaceans may prove tough reading for non-biologists. These animals are obscure and indeed almost unknown except to a very few specialists – who are possibly as weird as the copepods themselves. But they do not require magic insights to be appreciated. They are simply very small animals, often grotesquely shaped and leading amazingly adapted lives. With the help of the illustrations, I hope you enjoy them.

Finally, I gratefully acknowledge the varied contributions of many helpers, including especially Professor James Fairley and several of my colleagues in the Queen's University School of Biology and Biochemistry; Dr George Thoma (Washington DC); Dr David Erwin and Mr Bernard Picton (Ulster Museum); Mr Michael E Arfaras (Athens); Mr Robert Cussel (Canberra); Mr Thomas McGrath (Belfast). Karen Moore typed with limitless patience and expertise. I can only add that the encouragement of my own family – Gwyneth, David and Anthea – triumphed eventually over my sheer basic laziness. I thank them all.

Contents

Mychophilus: The Obsession of the Little Red Sausage

Mychophilus roseus

I don't know how obsessions arise, but this is the story of one that affected me for about 30 years. However, unlike many of its kind, it was resolved in the end, so that I could at last stop scratching at this particular mental itch.

The object of my preoccupation was a tiny marine crustacean. It has no common name but was scientifically christened *Mychophilus roseus* in 1865, having been discovered the year before between the tidemarks at Roscoff in Brittany. At this point (since not every reader, thank God, is likely to be a marine biologist) let me quickly supply a few technical details.

Our most familiar crustaceans, of course, are lobsters, crabs, prawns and other edible delicacies. Many other types exist, however, which we encounter less often. Among these are the copepods, small animals seldom exceeding two or three millimetres in length. Most are roughly pear-shaped and they swim and float in the sea in unimaginable profusion. It would be difficult to find one cubic metre of seawater anywhere in the world which lacks copepods – from which you will gather that their total numbers are indeed absolutely astronomical. They are, in fact, the commonest animals on earth and since many fish rely on them for food, they are of vital importance to the world's fisheries. So far about 12,000 species have been described and many more certainly await discovery. As well as these free-swimming copepods from oceans and lakes, over 3,000 species live as parasites and 'non-paying but tolerated guests' infecting fish, molluscs, sponges, marine worms, starfish and indeed almost every other type of aquatic animal, including other crustaceans. Important hosts are the animals popularly known as sea squirts. These unlikely looking creatures resemble small lumps of jelly which are permanently fixed to the seabed and which gently filter the water, extracting oxygen and minute items of food. Our copepod *Mychophilus* lives with two types of sea squirts which form colonies of individuals a few square centimetres in area and which generally grow on submerged rocks or seaweed. If you have survived this potted course in marine biology, we can now return to the story.

In the spring of 1948 my wife Gwyneth and I were helping to run a marine biology course at Portaferry, on the northeast coast of Ireland. We had been demobilized from the Royal Air

Lab work in the Portaferry marine station

Force some months earlier and were lecturing in the Zoology Department of Queen's University, Belfast, where we had been students in the early years of the war. We had married the previous August, thereby defying the predictions of numerous friends who were convinced that our apparently casual relationship of six years would persist unchanged forever. In this particular spring, I was surveying the small floating life (plankton) of Strangford Lough,

——— ❦ ———

while Gwyneth was researching the fauna of a tiny island, the Limestones, which becomes completely submerged at high tide. Since SCUBA equipment was then unavailable, we had to ensure that my newly acquired wife was plucked off the island by boat before she totally vanished beneath the next rising tide.

She was examining her haul one evening, using a small compact binocular microscope just acquired from America. In contrast to the 1870 German antiques we were accustomed to, this little instrument was superb for revealing (at remarkably high magnification) a magical microcosmic world. "What do you make of this?" she enquired after a long silence. I focused on to a tapestry of marvellously intermingled colours provided by colonies of two sea-squirt species. One was *Botryllus*, its individuals arranged in stars, all aglow with subtle shades of peacock blue and emerald green. The other was *Botrylloides*, its members side by side in gently curving lines and a brilliant rusty orange in colour. What took the breath away was that this tapestry was manifestly alive. Tiny currents of seawater were being inhaled and exhaled by the squirts, so that the whole scene shimmered

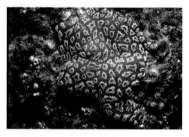

Colonial sea squirt Botryllus. *The small individual squirts are arranged in flower-like patterns set in the encrusting jelly.* (Photograph courtesy of Bernard Picton)

in slow motion. Minute fan worms in their spiral shells extended their tentacles and the occasional sea mite plodded cautiously across the stage. It was none of these, however, which had caught Gwyneth's attention.

Crawling very slowly through one of the transparent canals in the sea squirt colony was a tiny animal, less than 2mm long. It was uncannily like a minute mobile sausage – to be strictly accurate, a beef sausage, since it was rose-red in colour. Near it lay some small spheres of the same shade, which could only be its eggs.

On carefully extracting it from the sheltering canal, some more features were revealed. A few tiny, blunt protrusions could be seen, as well as a little twinkling eye at one end. Periodically, a small circular crater would open in the middle of its back and minute excretory fragments would drift out. I had never before seen an animal dispose of its waste from this location and the performance greatly intrigued me. What sort of a beast were we dealing with?

In this hunt for its identity, we combed our memories of the marine invertebrate groups. Some were easily eliminated, but a surprising number remained as possible relatives. Somewhere at the back of my mind a small persistent voice kept muttering, "Can it be a bizarre parasitic copepod?" – but it was all far too vague. After exhaustive speculation, fuelled by a lot of coffee, it became obvious that we badly needed help. It was time to call out the Fifth Cavalry.

In this context, the Fifth Cavalry meant a remarkable Norwegian biologist, Georg Ossian Sars. He had died at the age of 90 about 20 years earlier and devoted much of his time to chronicling the crustaceans of Norway. His numerous volumes were (and still are) a must in any marine laboratory, particularly because of his fine illustrations. His father, Michael, had also been a distin-

Female "little red sausage"
(Mychophilus). Head, with
small black eye on left; legs
visible on lower surface.

guished zoologist and, to complete the picture, his sister became the wife of the legendary polar explorer Fridtjof Nansen – 'Nansen of the North'. Anyhow, backing my hunch that our strange little animal might perhaps be a heavily disguised copepod, I leafed through the appropriate volumes. At this stage, I was only 'looking at the pictures' – something which no professional is supposed to do, but which everyone in fact does. On plate 36 the answer came up. There, unmistakably, was our animal, listed by

Sars as *Mycophilus roseus.* You will see here that the great man committed a minor error, since the copepod's original describer Eugene Hesse had put an extra "h" in the first (generic) name, making it *Mychophilus.* In broad translation this means a 'friend of slimy places' – not inappropriate to a copepod found only in the jelly-like sea squirts. In my early studies, I must admit to following Sars' spelling – I suppose because I didn't believe that the maestro could possibly be wrong.

Our discovery in Strangford Lough was the first Irish record of this species. It had been found a couple of times in Scotland, occasionally on the western coasts of Europe and in the western Mediterranean. Virtually nothing was known of its biology.

Intrigued by this lack of information, I began an intensive hunt around the shores of Strangford. It soon became clear that *Mychophilus* was quite common in its two sea squirt hosts, up to 20% of which were infected. Sometimes a few of our students would join in the search, greatly preferring these limited expeditions (which terminated in the local pub) to the three-hour frozen stints associated with more formal shore collecting. At all events, plenty of our little red sausages became available for detailed study.

Work in the marine laboratory. The student is Fergus McCullough, who later became a leading authority in west Africa on the highly dangerous tropical disease schistosomiasis which is caused by a parasitic worm.

In those days lab facilities on the collecting site at Portaferry were almost non-existent. Gallons of seawater had to be transported 30 miles by car to the University in Belfast and stored in a cold room, so that our catch could be examined alive. As long as the temperature was low enough and the host sea squirts remained healthy, *Mychophilus* pursued its customary tranquil existence. The only jarring note was that this was a strictly unisexual life-style. In all the scores of colonies examined over the subsequent years, every copepod was female – not a male was in sight!

I think it was at this stage that my obsession began. Here we had a thriving population – but half of it remained invisible. In copepods, as in most other animal groups, the sex ratio is more or less equal and males and females are generally similar in form, except for a few structural differences which can be easily seen. This applies to the great majority of free-swimming species, but in copepods strongly committed to a parasitic life-style, the picture can be very different. Not infrequently the female develops into an adult quite unlike that of a 'typical' copepod, often finishing up as a shapeless egg-producing bag. Males, on the other hand, may mature into an active swimming type, unmistakably copepodan in appearance, or else become small sperm-producing dwarfs attached to (or hidden in) the female's body. There are a few other rarer and more exotic variations on this theme of sexual difference but these need not concern us here.

I published a couple of papers on the general biology of the species and continued to search the host sea squirts whenever possible. Very occasionally some juveniles were found, but of the adult male there was still no trace. One reason for my persistence was the fact that in strongly parasitic forms, males usually offer far more clues as to the copepod's relationship with other allied families than the bizarrely adapted females.

As time passed, two new species of *Mychophilus* were described – one from the Red Sea in 1967 and one from the Straits of Gibraltar in 1996. Both were found in colonies of *Botrylloides*. These new members of the genus have a much longer 'tail end' than *Mychophilus roseus*. I mention this elongated 'tail' because when I first studied the copepod I won a small bet with a colleague who reckoned it was impossible to detect any difference between specimens obtained in *Botryllus* from those inhabiting *Botrylloides*. On being tested I won the bet easily since, to a practiced eye, the copepods from *Botrylloides* sported a fractionally longer 'tail'. At the time, I suggested that this might imply that we had two forms which were starting to differentiate into separate species. Perhaps the two new species from the Red Sea and Gibraltar (both, significantly, from *Botrylloides*) represent further steps along this evolutionary path.

So, back to the old obsession: where was the male? The answer only came at the end of my university career. There was a nice symmetry about this, since the study of the *Mychophilus* female was my first major piece of work thirty years earlier. A few months before I retired in 1984, a small parcel arrived from Dublin. It contained some preserved copepods just collected at various localities around the Irish coast at depths between 5 and 20 metres. These had all been captured in an ingenious underwater light-trap invented by a friend and colleague Mark Holmes (National Museum of Ireland) working in collaboration with James O'Connor.

After dark, the underwater world is a strange place. Many animals, large and small, swim to the surface at sunset and remain active through much of the night. A number of these are powerfully attracted to light and hence the considerable success of the Holmes/O'Connor traps. Mark's copepods were small, less than 1.3mm long – and all were males. At first sight they meant nothing to me, until I increased the magnification and looked at the tiny structures surrounding the mouth. One by one, they swam into focus – little replicas of the mouth parts which I had gazed at for 30 years on our sausage-like females! Here, at last, was the indubitable adult male of *Mychophilus roseus*. It had taken 120 years to be discovered.

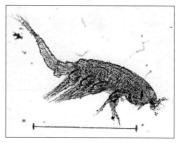

The adult male of the "little red sausage" (Mychophilus) in side view. The head is pointing to lower right. The length of the copepod is slightly over 1mm.

I tried to visualise exactly what this little male has to achieve in order to reach his mate. Lying in the depths of the sea squirt colony and incapable of surviving the world outside, the female must rely on his ability to detect her presence and penetrate the fortress. Over the years of searching and speculating, I had really come to imagine this event as something akin to that portrayed in Tennyson's *Daydream*. You remember the story? The beautiful princess is in a hundred-year sleep deep in the castle with all its varied life in total suspended animation. At last the prince arrives, seeks out her bedchamber – and there she is!

> *'A touch, a kiss! The charm was snapt!*
> *There rose a noise of striking clocks,*
> *And feet that ran, and doors that clapt,*
> *And barking dogs and crowing cocks;*
> *A fuller light illumined all,*
> *A breeze thro' all the garden swept,*
> *A sudden hubbub shook the hall,*
> *And sixty feet the fountain leapt.'*

It was only when we viewed our specimen under the probing beam of the scanning electron microscope that we realised how supremely equipped was this small male to outdo the exploits of Tennyson's ardent prince. On its under surface, at the head end, dozens of tiny pores, their rims delicately sculptured, penetrated the skin. From each pore a very long thin filament emerged to lie like tangled hair in the surrounding water beneath the copepod. What little we already knew from recent research on the sensory abilities of copepods clearly suggested that these fragile threads were receptive structures adapted to pick up and interpret fleeting biochemical clues as to what lay on the seabed. Not any old biochemical clues, you understand. Only those indicating the presence of the 'right' sea squirt host and whether that host was harbouring a receptive female *Mychophilus*. If the augurs were good, the male would enter the colony and inseminate the female with a package of sperms. Ingenious? You can say that again!

What is perhaps a little humbling is the reflection that our own technology for rapid signalling and communication has only really developed in little more than a century. Yet here we have a crustacean, less that 2mm long and of no great significance to anyone except itself, which has been using this incredibly refined detection method for (at a conservative estimate) a hundred million years – and that simply to locate his mate. Love conquers all, as Jimmy Durante used to sing.

Head-on view of the male Mychophilus roseus. *The very small tangled white threads dangling below the body are sensory receptors, probably used to locate the female.*

So my obsession ended after 30 years. I can think of no reason why this obscure crustacean became so important to me and can only plead the observation of Samuel Johnson. On being twitted by the insufferable Boswell for his avidity in gathering detailed information, the doctor finally replied: *"Sir,"* he said, *"there is no fact so trivial that I would rather not know it".*

A group of students and staff. Gywneth and I are first and second from left, front row.

I never called my mother Mummy, although we were always very close. I think responsibility for the omission lies with another woman, Takabuti. She was an Egyptian, the daughter of a priest of Amun and lived about 2,700 years ago. Her eternity, however, has now included well over a century in the Ulster Museum. I first laid eyes on her when I was very small, but afterwards visited her occasionally like an old friend who, remarkably, never changes. Takabuti was my first mummy – indeed the first dead person I ever saw – but I never thought of her as being dead. I just didn't want to associate her in any way with my own maternal parent. Besides, there was something a little odd about her. Picture books had shown me ancient Egyptians who were clad in what I thought rather attractive outfits; who had masses of dark hair and seemed healthily sunburnt. By contrast, Takabuti was enshrouded in a long white wrapping with blue beads, was apparently a blonde (a *blonde*, for goodness sake!) and had black skin. It took me some time to discover that this colour was due to a preservative layer of pitch.

The fascination of museums is, of course, that they make the past real in a very material sense. But, unconsciously, they sometimes do more, by revealing a state of mind in the chief character, engendered by the event commemorated. I came across a nice example of this a few years ago when, with a couple of hours to spare, I wandered into the British Museum. It was featuring an exhibition centred on the life of Nelson and included his last note to Emma Hamilton, written on the evening before Trafalgar.

Nelson's faded but legible scribble includes a reference to the Cape itself. The interesting point is that he has misspelt, of all words, Trafalgar! What he has in fact written is "Traflagar".

I have never seen this pointed out before. Published versions give the correct spelling in so-called verbatim quotes – yet in the original note, Nelson's tiny slip is perfectly clear.

It seems to me unlikely that the admiral was simply a bad speller. But how many of us, in moments of stress or profound distraction, occasionally transpose adjoining letters when we dash off a hasty message? I've done this often enough to be convinced that it is a real feature of human behaviour under present or imminent strain. Was Nelson really as calm and calculating as we generally suppose? Reflect on the next (and final) twenty-four hours of his life. Outnumbered and outgunned, his squadron was to fight at close quarters and beat the combined French and Spanish fleets. At a crucial stage of this enormously significant battle, he was to sustain a severe wound from a sniper's bullet and to die within a matter of hours. Talk about pressure! No wonder this pathetic little love letter has that small telltale error.

The museum I knew best was that of the Zoology Department at Queen's University. It comprised two big adjacent halls at the front of the original university building, but the second floor in both was limited to a balcony fronting an array of showcases. On the ground floor were large storage cabinets containing drawers and shelves. Each drawer had become in effect a lumber-room for small material not used in the teaching collection. For as long as anyone could remember there had never been a museum curator. The drawers had remained closed and inviolate.

In the immediate post-war years Gwyneth and I were the first to examine and sort much of this neglected material. Quite a number of specimens had been obtained and identified by Charles Wyville Thomson. This famous pioneer of oceanography had held the Chair of Natural History and Geology at Queen's between 1860 and 1870. He had stored some of his specimens in fragments of ancient newspaper, now as friable as the Dead Sea scrolls. These wrappings in themselves held a certain charm. An Aberdeen paper, in the spring of 1859, advertised the imminent departure for Melbourne of '*The Very Fast Clipper ship* Lord Raglan *(477 tons) with poop cabin accommodation for a few Families*'. Another, a '*Splendid New A1 British-built barque*' was sailing to Quebec on 1st April. Its passengers had conveyed to the Captain that "*they were highly satisfied with the easy sailing of the Ship*". There was even, bizarrely, an Independent Chapel for sale in Aberdeen seating 500 persons, at a '*Reduced Upset Price*'. One can only speculate what a reduced upset price would have meant over a hundred and fifty years ago in this Scottish city of legendary financial acuity.

Unfortunately, little of Thomson's zoological material would have been worth saving. However, a more spectacular exhibit was a very large and badly stuffed polar bear. This was, historically speaking, a rather famous beast, having been shot on one of the abortive expeditions which had set out to look for Sir John Franklin, whose party had vanished in the Arctic wastes while seeking the North-West passage. The bear's condition had not improved over the years. Its broad back formed a convenient landing stage for zoology students disinclined to circumnavigate the upper gallery and negotiate a narrow stairway to the lower level. Hanging by the arms, it was possible to drop straight onto the bear and thereby save a few moments while rushing to the next lecture. Its pelt, though superficially luxuriant, was in fact of thistledown fragility. A zealous museum assistant, who once attempted to vacuum-clean the fur, had the unique experience of witnessing what appeared to be a good third of this enormous animal vanish up the tube before the machine could be switched off.

At that time, the museum also housed a large collection of exotic stuffed birds. In biologically improbable postures, they occupied shelf after shelf of dusty, glass-fronted cupboards. They also figured prominently in one bizarre incident. The Vice-Chancellor of the day had announced one of his periodic University inspections – events departmentally regarded in the same light as natural catastrophes. "I like", he had proclaimed on a recent visit to Chemistry, "to see lots of shining glass". This obsession created an atmosphere of panic-stricken gloom in Zoology, where acres of the stuff, opaque with the grime of ages, were only too evident. Our Chief Technician, a man well versed in the psychology of senior administrators, saved the day. Armed with a filthy duster, he quickly polished only the outward-facing glass eye of every bird in the collection. The resulting beady points of reflected light shone brilliantly through the murk of the totally undusted display cases. Seemingly hypnotized by this firmament of avian eyes, the Vice-Chancellor completed his tour in docile silence, afterwards complimenting the Department on its outstanding cleanliness.

Queen's also possessed a fine assortment of marsupial material. T.T. Flynn, Professor of Zoology between 1931 and 1948, who came to the Chair from the University of Hobart, Tasmania, supplied much of this. His research field was marsupial embryology – an interest unlikely to be pursuable amongst the unpouched fauna of the Ulster countryside. Although a fine first-year lecturer and a good embryologist, Theo Flynn was inevitably destined to be known simply as 'Errol Flynn's father'. Errol did, in fact, pay one visit to Belfast, before his full blossoming as a Hollywood star. At a party to mark his arrival, he succeeded in spiking the orange juice of a teetotal (and very senior) academic wife with a massive slug of gin. The result, spectacular beyond all expectation, ensured his subsequent exclusion from University festivities.

The old museum has gone now – or rather it has undergone a metamorphosis into administrative offices. When the Department moved to more modern but less spacious quarters, the collections were broken up. A few specimens were retained, some given away, many destroyed. To visit their former home is a curious experience – computers hum where primeval silence prevailed; strip lighting has replaced the softer shafts of a westering sun. Perhaps one should return to the place only after dark. Maybe then the old familiar shapes would re-emerge: the elephant skeleton encrusted with student signatures, the bear who died because Franklin vanished, the sad, exotic fowl. And perhaps the beneficent ghost of Wyville Thomson is there too, cataloguing yet again his treasured sea snails from the forgotten voyages of long ago.

A War in Shangri-La

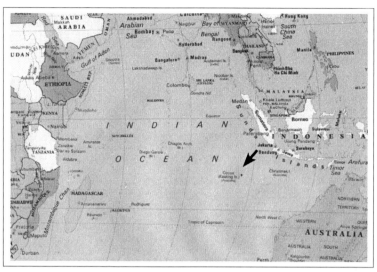

Map showing the position (arrowed) of the Cocos Keeling Islands in the Indian Ocean. (Adapted from Philip's World Atlas, George Philip Ltd.)

World wars are great engines of destiny. Get embroiled in one, for whatever reason and your life is shaped for the duration by sheer fate. Horrific places and actions, normally avoided like the plague, become commonplace. But, just occasionally, the dice fall differently. The horrors are miraculously suspended and enchanted surroundings embrace you in a peaceful, if temporary, cradle.

I experienced this rarely encountered phenomenon for no less than six months at the end of 1944, when I was sent to the Cocos Keeling Islands in the Indian Ocean. These certainly qualify for the adjective 'remote'. Situated 12°11' S, 96°50' E, they lie approximately 600 miles west of Java and Sumatra, 1,500 miles northwest of Australia and about the same southeast of Sri

Lanka. But I had better explain first how this serendipitous event came about.

Early in 1944, Gwyneth and I joined the Royal Air Force. Political considerations had ruled out conscription in Northern Ireland, so every recruit (and there were many) was a volunteer. Apart altogether from 'moral' or 'patriotic' reasons, I think we had the feeling we just might be missing out on some unique and momentous life experience. It was this fear, rather than any identification with Shakespeare's *"Gentlemen in England now a-bed shall think themselves accursed they were not here,"* which led to this temporary abandoning of academic life. Admittedly, there was also a sneaky feeling that in the post-war world, jobs might be more easily obtained if one could claim some experience of military service. Gwyneth's honours degree, plus a good track record in mathematics, led to her commission as a meteorological officer after a brief training period in the ranks. Although I sported a pass degree in zoology, I had a great reluctance to seek a commission, as I felt it would involve me in responsibilities I had absolutely no wish to shoulder. Moral cowardice, you may rightly say – but at least better than Evelyn Waugh's serviceman in *Put out more flags* who refused a commission because it would involve

mixing with the officers. Anyway, I too elected to serve in the meteorological section with the exalted rank of Aircraftman, 2nd Class.

Nine months later, I was on board the S.S. Windsor Castle, heading for an unknown destination. The Allied invasion of Europe had started to push the Axis forces back. The battle for the Indo-Pacific, however, was still blazing away, so clearly we were

Part of the 713 Forecast Centre, RAF, Sri Lanka. I am (arrowed) in the back row.

bound for somewhere in that vast area. Our first stop proved to be Bombay, with a month in a large transit camp. Then came a sea-passage in an incredibly broken down coaster to Sri Lanka

—— ❧ ——

(still named Ceylon in those days) and finally a posting to Galle, a remote little town on the island's southern tip.

I was there for only a few days when, in the late evening, I led the night shift into the met office. The squadron leader looked up and beckoned me into his inner office. "What I am going to say," he said, "is top secret. You are not to mention it to anyone. Tomorrow night I am sending you to Brown."

"Good God," I exclaimed, "the Cocos Islands!"

"Don't even whisper those words," he said irritably. "How did you know that Brown was their code name?"

"I thought everyone did," I said mildly, "but it's good news. Cocos – I mean Brown – is a famous location for marine biology. It was there that Darwin began to develop his theory about the formation of coral reefs."

"I am glad you're pleased," he said dubiously.

"Why did you pick me?" I asked.

"Because tonight you were the one who came through the door first." There was no answer to that one, so I waited. "I wanted to be completely unbiased," he muttered, "since I am probably sending you to your death." I looked at him. He seemed quite normal – for a man, that is, who had just uttered that classic statement.

"How's that?" I ventured after a few seconds' stunned silence.

"Work it out for yourself," he said plaintively. "The Japanese are occupying Java, Sumatra and Christmas Island to the east. They've also taken the Andamans to the north. There is nothing to stop them at Cocos, no defences – and it's an important cable link to Australia. You're going alone to replace an Australian Air Force meteorologist who's gone down with appendicitis and been flown back home. You will clear this station in the morning. Make sure you draw a Sten gun from the Armoury. There's a Catalina leaving for the islands tomorrow night."

I spent the next day immersed in the ritual of 'clearing the station.' This meant handing everything back to the various sections and obtaining signatures. At the Armoury, I tried to bargain my way up to a Bren gun. Although no gun addict, I liked the Bren. It was a lovely smooth gun to fire. By contrast, the Sten gun was cheap, nasty and kicked like a mad horse. It was wildly inaccurate, which probably enhanced its appeal as a terrorist weapon.

"I am not wasting a Bren on you," snorted the Armoury sergeant.

"How about some ammo?" I suggested.

"I am not giving you any ammo," he replied blandly. "Now pick up your gun and f—off!" I did so. At least I would have something solid to throw at a Japanese landing party.

That night, I boarded the Catalina flying boat in the brief tropical dusk and settled down in the amidships blister. Everything was still; the sea was bronze as we taxied out. The engines hummed slowly into full power, our hull split the bronze and gently we disengaged ourselves to float south beneath the stars. Interminably the night passed. As dawn broke over a limitless ocean, the atoll appeared. Its lagoon was translucent green and the surrounding islets, their seaward edges lipped with sparse foam, were dark with coconut palms. We glided down and tied up near a little pier on Direction Island. With the engines killed, the silence seemed absolute. All at once this small still world of colour was pervaded by a powerful sense of total unreality.

Captain William Keeling had 'officially' discovered these islands around 1608-09 when commanding an East India ship. There seems little to recount over the next two centuries until Scottish sea captain John Clunies Ross made a landfall while en route to India in 1825. Ross evidently liked what he saw, for after planting a Union Jack on one of the islands, he paid a return visit in 1826, accompanied by eight sailor-artisans, his wife and family and his wife's mother, a Mrs Dymoke. Here, surely, was a man of unusual personality, prepared to isolate himself on a remote coral island with his mother-in-law! To his surprise, however, he discovered that he was not alone. Another Briton, Alexander Hare, formerly governor of a remote area of Borneo, was already installed, along with a harem of forty Malaysian women. Ironically, it was Ross's brother Robert who had transported them to Cocos, quite unaware of John's plan to settle there.

Ross and Hare were ill-suited neighbours. As Ross's party expanded their foothold on the atoll, Hare and his women retreated, ultimately confining themselves to a small castle-like building on Prison Island, a tiny fragment of land between two of the larger islands. But relations deteriorated further, Hare's women finally deserting him to seek Ross's protection. Hare then abandoned his project and sailed off to Djakarta.

Freed from this distraction, Ross started to construct his little island empire. With a workforce of Malaysians and Javanese, he founded a copra industry, built a large mansion, imported a doctor and evolved a unique social system, including his own currency, which originally consisted of coins made of whalebone. Presumably to avoid contamination from the outside world, he drew up an interesting contract with his workers. Anyone could leave the island if they so wished – but if they did, they could never return! Shangri-La had come to the Indian Ocean.

In 1886, Queen Victoria granted Cocos to John's son George, so the family continued as virtual rulers. By the late eighteen-nineties it was home to about a thousand people and was listed as a dependency of the Straits Settlements. In 1955, however, Queen Elizabeth (who had briefly visited the atoll in the previous year) withdrew Victoria's indenture and transferred the islands to Australian control. The final act in the Clunies Ross connection came when the great great grandson of the founder (another John) was bought out of his copra industry by the Australian government. He invested the profit in a shipping company but eventually had to hand over the ancestral mansion on Home Island to the trustee of his estate in 1988. A family commitment of unusual romantic appeal had ended.

The Cocos group consists of five islands large enough to be inhabited and about 22 much smaller islets. To the north lies Horsburgh guarding the entrance to the lagoon, Direction Island with its Cable and Wireless station, where I was billeted for six months and, close to it, Home Island with the Ross mansion and the workers' village. The other side of the six mile wide lagoon is flanked by South Island and the largest of the group, West Island, about seven miles long. With a mean temperature of around 80°F and an annual rainfall of about 70 inches a good variety of plants occur, as well as the ubiquitous coconut palms. These all thrive despite not infrequent exposure to severe cyclones.

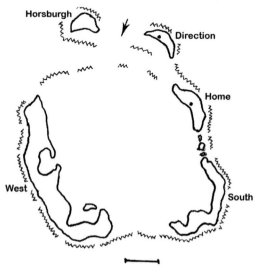

The Cocos atoll in the east Indian Ocean. Black dot on Direction Island indicates the Cable and Wireless Station. Black dot on Home island indicates the Clunies Ross mansion. Arrow shows the entrance to the lagoon. vvv *indicate coral reefs. Scale=1 mile.*

Keeling Island which, so far as I know, has never been regularly inhabited, lies 18 miles north of the main (Cocos) group. In the past, it was a great breeding ground and refuge for birds.

The Cable and Wireless station, established on Direction Island in 1901, was housed in a series of low wooden buildings with corrugated iron roofs, each room having a small private balcony overlooking the lagoon less than a hundred yards away. I was allocated the room lately occupied by the appendicitis victim and quickly settled into the routine. My fellow meteorologist was

Sergeant Jim Hollingsworth who hailed from Tasmania and we took alternate days on duty. The work could not be described as arduous, simply involving general weather observations about four times a day, plus setting up and recording by theodolite the flight of a hydrogen-filled met balloon in the middle of the night. This latter operation could be frustrating since it meant attaching a small candle in a Chinese lantern to

Direction Island, Cocos atoll 1944, showing the Cable and Wireless building on the shore of the lagoon.

the balloon. At the critical moment of release, the candle would quite frequently blow out and the whole tiresome routine would have to be undertaken again.

The Cable and Wireless men were ethnically mixed, though mainly Australian. The Head of Station was Mr Moss (whose first name I've forgotten), a very pleasant Australian who had married a girl from Northern Ireland. Not only that, but she had gone to the same school in Coleraine as Gwyneth. To cap the coincidence, her younger sister had become Gwyneth's best school friend. This, of course, gave us an immediate link.

Another Aussie who still floats vividly in my memory after 55 years was Izzy Towner, a small, spare man with an enormous black beard and large horn-rimmed glasses. He was a superb classical pianist with a special penchant for Chopin. In what passed for a recreation room there was, surprisingly, an excellent grand piano and I would sit and listen as Izzy wandered through his extensive repertoire. It was a remarkably soothing experience.

There was another Australian with whom I went fishing, two Englishmen and a Singhalese. Their faces I recall perfectly but not, alas, their names. A staff recruited from the villagers of Home Island met our domestic needs and we also enjoyed the services of a magnificent Chinese cook. Every Sunday he would produce an unbelievable lunch. Pigs and fowl were reared on Home Island, while the lagoon provided unending species of fish as well as molluscs and crustaceans. Pawpaws and other fruit grew abundantly and there was certainly no shortage of coconut. If my met officer in Sri Lanka thought he was sending me to my death, it would have been engendered by over-eating, rather than at the hands of the Japanese.

As regards the military wanderings of the latter, they still failed to materialise but their arrival at Cocos was constantly expected. A few weeks before I arrived, two medium bombers passed low over Direction and dropped a couple of bombs, causing craters near our building but no real damage. Very shortly after this unimpressive raid, the reigning Clunies Ross died, with his heir apparent still a boy at school in England. I don't know what evidence, if any, was to hand, but the Cable and Wireless staff had an intriguing and quite tenable theory to explain those events. They told me that before the Japanese declared war, they sent a deputation to Cocos requesting fishing rights around the atoll. Ross granted this, but with the proviso that should hostilities break out, the islands would remain inviolate. This was apparently agreed and Japanese vessels duly appeared in the area. It seemed, however, that their main quarry was not fish, but the salvaging of a wreck on Keeling Island. This wreck was that of the first World War German cruiser *Emden*, of which more later. Rumour had it that large quantities of potentially valuable scrap metal quickly disappeared into Japanese holds. The bombing of Direction Island, however, though feeble in the extreme, had struck Ross as a direct violation of his 'treaty' with Japan and the shock might well have contributed to his death a few days later.

We had frequent discussions as to possible courses of action should the Japanese overrun our island, which was less than a mile long and about 300 yards in width. Views differed, but all were contingent on our having some degree of warning. A couple of the staff decided that with some facial make-up they might be able to melt into the workers' village. Another reckoned that he could hide out on the relatively large uninhabited West Island and live off the land. I joined a group who were determined to flee the atoll in one of our small boats and head for northwest Australia – but I fervently hoped that none of these over-optimistic scenarios would have to be put to the test.

So how did we spend our time in this idyllic but threatened little world? As far as the cable staff was concerned, it was a 'no-wives' station. To compensate, good Scotch whisky (and any other drink you care to name) was incredibly cheap. Most nights, you could party in someone's room. Up to then, my drinking habits had been fairly naïve and certainly moderate. But the heat, inevitable boredom and underlying anxiety about our immediate destiny, plus Australian drinkers experienced to a degree of near-immunity, made the prolonged evening sessions hard to resist. So it was not difficult to find something to worry about. Several of my relatives, on both sides of the family, though not actual alcoholics, were certainly mildly addicted to the stuff. As I looked forward to yet another evening's festivities, I found it almost impossible to avoid treating myself to a preliminary snort from my own supplies. The whole syndrome was becoming too like Somerset Maugham for comfort. Eventually I compromised – again, I suppose, classically – by not opening the bottle before sunset. Watched eagerly, the sun would balance on the horizon, then slowly vanish (sometimes even eliciting that famous 'green flash') before I rushed to my cupboard.

During Christmas week of 1944, I wandered around performing the normal meteorological duties with a permanent slight hangover. Perhaps the partial anaesthesia thus achieved was not a bad thing, for with the new year came appalling news from home. We had just received one of the wildly erratic mail deliveries dropped by Catalina and I had settled down for a nostalgic wallow. There was a letter from Gwyneth. She had managed to get a couple of days leave and had picked up an airlift to Belfast. She had made the five-minute walk from her parents' home to mine, arriving to hear that my sister had just been killed in an

air crash. Priscilla was four years older than I and we were very close. This was a first family death and I was shattered by its impact. What made the whole affair more bearable was the enormous measure of sympathy and concern that I received from my island mates. These outwardly tough characters whom I had known for only a month could not have been kinder and more considerate. At the risk of sounding trite, they really did restore my faith in human nature.

My sister, Priscilla (Army Transport Auxiliary Service); killed in a military air crash, November 1944

On my days off, I made a half-hearted effort to keep fit by swimming in the lagoon and walking on the reef flats at low tide. Another welcome diversion was a concrete tennis court behind the main building. Five years earlier, I had represented Northern Ireland as a junior player but the war had put a stop to any further competitive play. However, it was fun to hit a few balls again with a borrowed racket.

This tennis court had acquired a unique history during the first world war and brings us back to the German cruiser *Emden*. When war broke out in August 1914, *Emden* slipped south into the Atlantic to begin a brief but astonishingly successful career as a surface raider. Entering the Indian Ocean she managed, in less than three months, to sink fifteen allied ships and to capture another eight merchantmen. This included an attack on Penang off the Malaysian coast where she sank a Russian cruiser and a French destroyer. The victims were taken by complete surprise, since *Emden* had fitted a false funnel, giving her a profile very similar to that of a British cruiser.

In October 1914 she appeared at another tiny Indian Ocean outpost, Diego Garcia. Here a benevolent French resident presented her with large quantities of eggs and fruit. It turned out that he was totally unaware that war had been declared two months earlier, but was startled by the obviously war-like status she maintained. *Emden's* captain, Karl von Müller, explained smoothly that his ship was currently engaged in 'German-French-British world naval manoeuvres' – a nice touch this and, in a strictly literal sense, true!

A month later, she met her Nemesis. She was short of fresh water and materialised off Cocos to renew her supplies. When she was spotted entering the lagoon, the telegraph staff at once flashed off news of her presence. This dramatic announcement was picked up by the Australian cruiser *Sydney*, which headed at full speed to the atoll.

The first act of the *Emden's* landing party was an attempt to fell the large telegraph mast, not realising that the fatal message had already gone out. When the wireless staff viewed the start of this operation, they protested to von Müller. If felled from this angle, the mast would crash down across their tennis court. The Captain responded with all the courteous naval chivalry for which he had become famous. Of course their tennis must not be impeded! We will make it fall in a different direction! At the cost of some delay, this was done – an act, incidentally, commemorated by a plaque beside the court. *Emden* replenished her supplies and prepared to leave, but the Sydney had now closed and was soon able to open fire. *Emden* fled north but had only made 18 miles and was badly crippled before beaching herself on the reefs of North Keeling Island. This final engagement had cost her crew 134 lives.

As a boy, I had been fascinated by the *Emden* story and it was intriguing to be at the very spot where its climax had been played out thirty years earlier. One day, an old native fisherman took me out in his boat and showed me how to bait a floating line with a crab's leg to catch flying fish. Our conversation was limited, but he remembered vividly the coming of the *Emden* and the dramatic hours which ensued. (He also introduced me to a delicious type of sweetened coconut bread – and the flying fish we caught were equally good.)

Some sporadic attempts had been made to sample some of the atoll's fauna following Darwin's brief visit aboard the *Beagle* in 1836, but these had yielded little of significance. Cocos enchanted Darwin and its marvellous reefs provided the inspiration for him to interpret their mode of origin. His theory remains by far the most plausible explanation, though more recent researches have shown that details may vary from one reef system to the next.

A more extended expedition was based on the atoll for 15 months in 1905-6 and quite a comprehensive collection was made by its leader, Felix Wood Jones. As might be expected in so remote and isolated a locality, the mammals were represented solely by rats – the great colonisers of the animal world. Interestingly, three types were apparently present. A population almost confined to Direction Island was already established when Clunies Ross set up his home in 1827. Incidentally, the native name for Direction is *Pulu Tikus* – 'Rat Island'. For 50 years, these rats remained, but in 1878 the ship *Robert Portner* was wrecked on the atoll and contributed a large legacy of *Rattus norvegicus*, the brown rat (cited by Jones as *Mus decumanus*). That noted ship traveller, the black rat (*Rattus rattus*) arrived later, as a result of further wrecks. Specific identity for the original (pre-1827) invaders remains uncertain, but it seems probable that prolonged isolation and inbreeding might have transformed some early castaway *R. norvegicus* or *R. rattus* into a visibly distinct type. The unique ecology of a coral atoll had evidently modified the behavioural patterns of these rats, since Captain Fitzroy of the *Beagle* noted that many rats made their nests on the tops of palm trees. In my time on Cocos, rats were certainly not a prominent element of the fauna.

The reptiles recorded by Wood Jones provide interesting examples of chance distribution. At least two specimens of the very large double-crested crocodile (*Crocodylus porosus*) were reported, one of which was shot. Although this widespread species is tolerant of salt water, it may well have made the greater part of a journey of not less than 600 miles as a passenger on floating driftwood. Such fortuitous rafts drifting down major rivers probably account for some unlikely occurrences of animals on remote islands. Several large snakes were similarly on record but none gained a foothold in this restricted habitat. Two species of gecko also figure in Wood Jones' list and one at least was still there forty years later. These lizards lay hard-shelled eggs which often take a long time to hatch and are generally deposited in crevices or holes in bark. They are, therefore, naturals for this method of transport by rafting.

The bird which remains most vividly in my memory is the small and delicate fairy tern (*Gygis candida*). Its black eyes, bill and feet contrast strongly with the purest of white plumage and it has the engaging habit of fluttering casually above one's head. Captain Joshua Slocum, who visited the atoll during his single-handed navigation of the globe in the 1890s, was fascinated by it, remarking that it was called by the islanders the *"pilot of Keeling Cocos"*. Darwin was equally enchanted: "Little imagination is required to fancy that so light a body must be tenanted by some wandering fairy spirit."

I will say little of my excursions over the reef flats and in the shallower parts of the lagoon. This is partly because great advances in underwater colour photography have by now made coral reefs and their inhabitants very familiar to an engrossed public. But it is also because I can find no words to describe the

Direction Island, Cocos atoll, 1944. Coral reef exploration party. From left: Jim Hollingsworth (Royal Australian Air Force), Izzy Towner (Cable and Wireless), myself (Royal Air Force) and a Singhalese colleague (Cable and Wireless).

mind-numbing impact the Cocos reefs had on me at that time. Half a century ago remote reefs were undisturbed by tourist traf-

———— ∞ ————

fic, unpolluted by industrial products, untouched by exploitative souvenir hunters. They were as pristine as the first day of creation. To a marine biologist whose experience was limited to the grey coastal waters of northern seas, the sparkling clarity of these warm waters, the vivid colours and graceful movements of innumerable fish, plus the rainbow background of crevices peopled by spectacular invertebrates was almost too rich a diet. What struck me above all was the sense of being surrounded by an atmosphere of absolutely impeccable taste. However bizarre a shape or movement, however dramatic or unexpected a colour pattern, everything fitted together so perfectly that each new scene seemed to say "This is what evolution is all about. This magic is what can be achieved."

This six-month holiday came inevitably to an end. The atoll was invaded, not by the Japanese, but by the Royal Air Force, who laid down a metal landing strip on West Island and established camp there. It was at that time envisaged that the war in the Indo-Pacific could well last for many more months. When my presence on Direction Island was discovered, I was summoned to West Island and reintroduced to the routine of station life. The transition was not one I relished.

I don't remember much of the next four months. At one stage we were caught by the edge of a cyclone and the phrase 'raining stair-rods' became all too real. In three feet of water we shifted enormous cylinders of hydrogen on to higher ground (not easy to find on a coral atoll) in the middle of an inferno of wind at three o'clock in the morning. Astride the cylinders with two other carriers, the illusion of manning a midget submarine was complete.

I also recall an extraordinary incident involving the Pay Accounts office and RAF security. After a few weeks on West Island, I called in at Pay Accounts to enquire how much pay had accumulated since I left Sri Lanka. This was sheer curiosity, since of course there was nothing to buy.

"How long have you been here?" I was asked.

———— ✧ ————

"Seven months" I replied.

The accounts clerk looked at me keenly. "You can't have been here that long," he said, "no one was here until four weeks ago."

"I was on one of the other islands since last December."

"Well," he said, "leave it for now and I'll have it investigated." I met him again a couple of weeks later. "You and your query threw Security into a right panic," he said. "They've had you secretly under surveillance for the last fortnight."

"Why did they do that?" I enquired.

"Well, you must admit you've got a rather odd name. Could be oriental, they thought and you might be a Japanese spy. However, they couldn't find anything incriminating." In the silence that followed, I wondered, not for the first time, how the hell we were ever going to win this war.

One other episode stands out starkly. One morning in early August I went on shift and was told by the forecaster that news had just come through that Hiroshima had been devastated by a single bomb. "Something special," he said, "an atomic bomb." I knew just enough physics to speculate whether the world would ever be the same again.

One day we were told that three Liberator bombers were taking off for Sri Lanka and would be transporting some of the met staff, including myself. I grabbed my belongings and climbed aboard. Our Liberator had been shot up on some recent mission and the repairs were obvious but fragmentary. We climbed to a cruising height of about 7,000 feet, with the wind whistling through the plane's battered body. It wasn't the only body it was whistling through; mine was clad only in shorts and a shirt and I was beginning to feel distinctly chilly. Then we ran into a weather phenomenon known as the ITF – Inter Tropical Front – which was bad news. Our two companion planes turned back for Cocos, but our pilot was made of sterner stuff. "I'm not going back to that sodding island," he announced, "I'm going up till we can climb out of this crap." He eventually achieved this at around 13,000 feet and held her there till the Sri Lankan coast came in sight several hours later. I went through every phase of gradual refrigeration until we landed at China Bay on the northeast coast. By that time I had the impression that my internal organs had frozen into a solid core of ice. Contrary to the feelings of euphoria which are alleged to accompany death by hypothermia, I found myself in a highly depressive state. The blissful early days on the atoll were now a world away and I felt isolated and miserable. Like Adam, I had been booted out of Paradise. Unlike Adam, there was no Eve at hand to console me.

A Zoologist in the Services

With my future wife, Gwyneth, 60 years ago.

The Cocos interlude played such a major part in my personal war that much of the remaining two years has tended to fade into an undefined blur. But since incidents, personalities and places occasionally haunt this antique shadow-land, a few may be worth recalling – not, God knows, from the viewpoint of military heroics but because, like many of my generation, I have often gone through the routine of explaining exactly what I did do during the War.

When hostilities began sixty years ago, Northern Ireland was a relatively distant target for the Nazi war machine and for the first eighteen months we were spared its attention. The initial shock of reality came at Easter 1941.

Gwyneth and I, both nineteen and rapidly falling in love, were on a marine zoology course at Portaferry on the shores of Strangford Lough. The university had rented a small shop on the sea front to act as a lab and we slept at various lodgings throughout the little town. I lodged with Mr and Mrs Primmer in an old Victorian terrace house in the square. Mr Primmer was the local coastguard, but had also signed up as Portaferry's air raid warden. One night, during a romantic walk in the ragged moonlight, a whistle being blown at regular intervals startled us. Mr Primmer had mounted his bicycle and was cruising through the streets sounding the air raid warning. A few moments later a squadron of bombers passed steadily overhead, using the long length of Strangford as a pointer to Belfast, twenty-five miles distant. Somewhat to my surprise, it was true that German aircraft engines did sound different.

This raid achieved only limited success. The chance presence of an aircraft carrier in the Belfast docks ensured that some effective anti-aircraft fire was available – just as well, since our local defences at that time were hopelessly inadequate. Our vulnerability was at least partially repaired as a sizeable number of barrage balloons were later installed and anti-aircraft batteries sited throughout the city. A balloon was tethered thirty yards from my grandmother's front door and greatly enlivened what was to prove her last year. Our defences were savagely tested a few weeks later.

In April and May the Luftwaffe targeted Belfast for two horrific nights. These raids, one following a fortnight after the other, destroyed 3,600 houses, damaged many other buildings and took about 1,100 lives. I had joined the Air Raid Precautions service and was sent on anti-looting patrol the night after the second raid. It was strange to walk through once familiar parts of town now reduced to twenty feet of smouldering rubble and to realise that under it must still lie the remains of my fellow-countrymen. My companion on this harrowing night was an elderly, lugubrious citizen of limited speech and imagination. As he poked experimentally at the debris, he repeated at half-minute intervals "City of the dead, city of the dead" till, by dawn, I felt like adding him to the list.

When I completed my degree and joined the Air Force, along with 104 other recruits, we were shipped over to Stranraer en route for the large RAF training camp at Padgate outside

Warrington. The train journey to camp was made memorable by the clandestine addition of massive quantities of laxative into the tea-urns at the Stranraer transit camp. Such wholesale medication was, of course, a regular feature of service life. Our Flight occupied two large carriages on the slow journey south, which meant that only four toilets were available to cope with 105 cases of prolonged diarrhoea. Constant kicking at locked toilet doors availed nothing – those within had no intention of abandoning their seat while waiting apprehensively for the next bout. To stay the course through all those long hours was virtually impossible. When the train at last pulled in, outraged NCOs awaiting the Flight insisted on the carriages being scrubbed clean and disinfected by the victims themselves. It was a gruesome introduction to service justice.

Training at Padgate (popularly known as the Belsen of England) was a voyage of self-discovery. I found, to my surprise, that although I was a good shot with the old army .303 rifle, I was an even better one when handicapped by a gas mask. Bayonet practice, however, was embarrassing in the extreme. Elderly sergeant instructors would plead for a convincing display of savagery. One by one, we would prance up to a sack of straw embellished, of course, with a cardboard face of Hitler and plunge the bayonet in with a blood-curdling yell. My initial delicate prodding and ferocious squeak would not do at all – so I had to ham up the whole performance. Much more frightening was our brief introduction to a live grenade. The same instructors insisted on a bowling action. Theoretically this may have been sound, but few of our Irish intake had ever played cricket. Anxiety to get rid of the missile led to many grenades being released from a sweaty hand far too soon. As they flew vertically upwards we would scatter at high speed before burrowing into the ground. Amazingly, there were no casualties.

Physical training was no riot of fun either. A pink-faced healthy PT sergeant, clad in windproof trousers and at least two large sweaters, would lead us at 7 am, dressed in PT vest and shorts, into an adjoining low-lying field which, at that hour in early March, was blanketed by two feet of mist. It was curious to see heads emerging from this white fog before collapsing into invisibility. Eventually, I succumbed to a nasty dose of what was known as 'Padgate Flu' and was hospitalized. Qualifying for several days sick leave, but banned from returning to Belfast, I headed for Windermere. This was not due to any marked preference

Gwyneth (Womens' Auxiliary Air Force), 1944.

for lake scenery, but simply because Gwyneth was there on her Officers' Training Course. In the event, private meetings were distinctly tricky. The small town was crawling with women officer cadets and their instructors. All were consciously and unbelievably smart in their uniforms. In an ill-fitting aircraftman's clobber, any close approach to Gwyneth resembled the tentative manoeuvres of a male spider in the presence of his mate – all very precarious. As one of Gwyneth's officers put it, the whole set up was like being discovered having an affair with your butler. However, in her free time, we hired bicycles and cruised around some of that fabulous countryside, including a visit to the Freshwater Biological Association's headquarters at Wray Castle. I also participated marginally in the cadets' sports activities, being roped in as referee for a friendly hockey fixture at Grange-over-Sands. My knowledge of hockey rules was rudimentary, but the trip involved a pleasurable journey on the floor of a lorry, walled in by twenty-two healthy female legs.

Late May 1944 found us together again in London, this time attending our respective courses in meteorology at Paddington. Gwyneth was stationed at St John's Wood and I was billeted at what had been the St Regis hotel in Cork Street, beside Piccadilly

Circus. Its upper stories extensively damaged in the blitz, the hotel had been taken over as an Air Ministry Unit.

It was during this period that the invasion of Europe began, as did the assault on London of rocket bombs (the V1s and later, V2s) fired from the continent. Through a lecture room window we watched the first of these devices come crashing down. At this point, we took them to be very small aircraft on a kamikaze mission and I felt a momentary sympathy for the presumed pilot. They came to have a weird effect on Londoners well accustomed to more conventional bombing. The unmistakable drone was followed by a sudden silence as the engine cut and the bomb fell in a steep curve. Then came the shattering explosion. Since targets were utterly random, there was a Russian roulette feeling of being lucky or unlucky. Auditory clues – engine note, silence, massive explosion – became very important in the timing of a quick rush for shelter and the final dive to flatten oneself. I remember a Punch cartoon which neatly summarised it: A typical street scene, with two Londoners in earnest discussion. All was normal, except that every person in sight and every dog and cat had one monstrously enlarged ear. The caption went 'It's all nonsense to suggest that these bombs have made any difference to us at all!'

In a few days the V1 onslaught reached a climax as the launching pads in France had not yet been overrun by the Allied invasion. One hectic night some of us were sent up to the flat roof of the St. Regis on fire-watching duty. The damaged roof sloped drunkenly over Cork Street, its parapet long since destroyed. From a height of about eighty feet the view over the centre of London became unbelievable as the raid developed and more and more V1s arrived from the east. What had started as a balmy summer evening over the capital darkened by midnight into Dante's inferno. The many rockets which slipped past the patrolling fighters over the Channel appeared first as small red glows in the distance, to which the London barrage deafeningly responded. The continuing crescendo of sound was physically painful but the excitement so intense that fear seemed excluded.

Adrenaline in large quantities would have been abundantly available that night! At dawn, one of the last rockets passed south of our roof about two hundred feet away, before nose-diving. On another afternoon Gwyneth and I had spent a couple of hours in a cinema and emerged as the sirens sounded and the rockets passed overhead. Obliquely across the road was a tube station which we made for at top speed. Unfortunately, this street section had just been freshly tarred and we plunged across it with that familiar nightmare sensation of trying to run in ankle-thick glue.

Activity in Cork Street was not confined to survival from air raids. One of the floors of a building immediately opposite the St. Regis was occupied by a large troop of beautiful, immaculately clad French girls. Although not attributable to any recognisable branch of the forces, they could legitimately be classified as Service girls – but their customers were financially elite. There was much window-to-window banter of a predictable sort across the narrow little street. "No, no!" they would shout in answer to queries, "we are much too expensive for you boys! We like only to entertain Americans." Sure enough, each dawn would see a selection of our transatlantic allies surreptitiously leaving the building.

When our Met courses finished, I was posted to Heathfield, a small naval airfield outside Ayr. For the moment, Gwyneth remained in London, much to my anxiety, as the V2 campaign had now started and these enormous rockets not only packed a formidable punch, but gave virtually no warning of their approach. However, five months at Heathfield passed pleasantly enough. The surrounding country greatly resembled my native County Down and it was only a short cycle ride to Burns' cottage and other peaceful places.

In November came a summons to Blackpool, one of the transit camps for overseas postings. After a couple of days indeterminate activity under the eye of England footballer Stanley Matthews (then an Air Force sergeant) we were told that embarkation was in 36 hours. A phone call to Gwyneth and we met in Manchester the following afternoon. I have no memory of what we did or talked about, but can recall a feeling that destiny was smoothly rolling us apart with no future guarantees. At last we said good-night on those tiers of steps which adorn Manchester's city hall. Even at this emotive moment (wouldn't you know it?) farce intervened. A policeman toiled up to view our last kiss. "You can't do that here" he said "Clear off; this is the city hall."

Early next morning we headed north for the Clyde and boarded the *Windsor Castle*, already packed with 2000 troops. It was a grey day, but as we steamed down the Irish Sea, the visibility lifted momentarily to the west and a fragment of the Irish coastline swam into view like a small dim vignette. In the centre was a low symmetrical hill on whose crest stood an abandoned windmill. I knew at once that it lay above our old stamping ground at Portaferry and was, in fact, one of our favourite walks. It remained in sight for only a minute until the visibility closed again and it vanished, like the farewell wave of an old friend.

So we come full circle to China Bay, which was to be my home for the next few weeks at the end of the Cocos saga. This naval base in northeast Sri Lanka seemed, for some unaccountable reason, to have a magnetic attraction for temporarily unemployed Met personnel. At one stage we had as many as twenty wandering around the office with very little to do. One result of this superfluous manpower stays in my memory. We had run out of Chinese lanterns which held the small candles below the night balloon. Rather than give up, I organised a large group of met assistants to join me in a firefly hunt. The little beetles with their powerful luminous organs were quite plentiful around the met office and not difficult to catch. When we had a couple of dozen, we broke off the socket of a clear electric light bulb and put the vigorously performing insects in, before plugging the top so that the overall weight approximated that of a Chinese lantern plus candle. We managed to follow our firefly balloon to a height of about 6,000 feet. In some dusty archive even now may perhaps lie the record of this blend of zoology with meteorology.

My next move was across country to Negombo, a large airfield hacked out of palm plantations about 30 miles north of the capital Colombo. Here, quite by chance, I met an old sporting acquaintance from Belfast. Robin was in the navy and we managed to have a few games of table tennis. Some years later, we regularly represented Ulster in the interprovincial tennis championships of Ireland.

When I reached Negombo, the camp was still being established. We slept in kadjan huts (largely made out of palm branches) and sanitary conditions were absolutely basic. Felled palm trunks had been propped at an angle across trenches floored with foliage and by walking cautiously out on these, you could, with some difficulty, relieve yourself into the ravine below. Until more civilised quarters were installed, the nights were disturbed by the despairing howls of those who overbalanced and plunged into the foliage beneath. Naturally enough, the final crash was usually followed by a burst of memorable obscenity. I mention this gruesome subject because, forty-three years later, I landed at Negombo for a fortnight's holiday. The surrounding palm trees were still there and I even glimpsed in a deserted corner what seemed to be the ruins of our old Flying Control tower. In this superbly equipped airport I sought out what proved to be the most luxurious toilet I had ever encountered, complete with soft, canned music, dimmed light and spotless tiles. The contrast was startling with my vivid memories of the same spot so long ago.

By the spring of 1946 the war had been over for eight months and a general election was looming in the United Kingdom. Those service personnel who had cherished dreams of being home a couple of months after the end of hostilities, were now sadly disillusioned. The sense of being 'used' by the government as cheap labour while wives and girlfriends were being wooed by carefree American servicemen back in the UK, moved easily from fantasy to a persistent, angry anxiety. It was against this background that the Labour party made a remarkably shrewd move. In camps throughout the middle and far eastern theatres appeared glib spokesmen whose theme was subtle and persistent. Didn't we all want to go home and be demobbed? If so, vote Labour, using your postal vote. A Conservative government would keep you out here indefinitely to service air transport companies at minimum cost. And aren't your parents, girlfriends, relatives anxious to welcome you home? So write to all of them, emphasizing that whatever their previous voting habits, only Labour would ensure your rapid return. A hurricane of mail followed this appeal and when the election of July 1946 resulted in an enormous Labour landslide, we were not in the least surprised. The fact that it seemed to make no difference to the rate of demobilisation, however, increasingly provoked feelings of extreme, cynical bitterness.

In a short time, the situation predictably exploded. Negombo was at the southern end of a teleprinter link which pushed up through India and extended west to stations in the Middle East. Suddenly word came through from the wireless operators that major air force stations on the northern and western links had gone on strike for faster demobilisation. There was plenty of emotional tinder at our end and Negombo promptly downed tools in support. Many of the officers were clearly sympathetic but could hardly say so. Commanding officers took various lines. Some were placatory, promising to do what they could. Others blustered, with threats that usually included the phrase "line you up and shoot you". As the Chinese say, it was an interesting time to live in, since it could hardly be denied that this was, in effect, mutiny pure and simple, its only redeeming feature being that the war was, in fact, long since over. In the event, some arrests were made and a few ringleaders actually jailed. Personally, I did not believe that the strike would achieve much – but there was no point in sitting in an empty met office. A couple of days later, a few of us were sent to the Colombo office, which was still operating. I never knew whether this meant that I was too dangerous to leave in the bush, or else was regarded as 'reliable'. Things eventually calmed down, after promises and guarantees were received from London and I returned to Negombo. If this little-remembered episode held any lessons for history, it at least made it clear that armed forces consisting largely of drafted men could not be treated like their forerunners.

Back at Negombo, I was due for a weekend leave and walked the half-mile from the camp to a rest house beside the beach. Here it was possible to relax, swim, read and indulge in some Sri Lankan food and drink. I helped some Tamil fishermen unload their outriggers after a night's fishing and watched the catch cascading on to the sand. The men were busy with a pile of large prawns, very similar to our own Dublin Bay prawn or Norway lobster. For some reason they were separating them into males and females, but were using a method quite unknown to me and which I found difficult to follow. However, they were every bit as quick as I was to sort out the sexes.

On my second night at the rest house, a solitary American appeared and we had a meal and a drink together. It was only as he was leaving that I discovered his identity. He was Paul Gallico, author of *The Snow Goose*, a book which was starting to enjoy worldwide popularity.

As I went back to camp, I walked through one of my favourite places, a tiny village on the edge of an old coconut plantation. Among the surviving palms were grouped about twenty kadjan huts, each encircled by a minuscule garden with vegetables, fruit and a few bright flowers. In the gentle dappled sunlight the inhabitants unhurriedly pursued their tranquil existence. The odd thing was that everything seemed to be on a miniature scale – the dwelling huts were tiny, the attendant dogs and cats were mostly in the puppy or kitten stage, the numerous children playing in the warm dust were for the most part toddlers. There was the occasional baby goat and the delicate little palm squirrels which flitted across the scene appeared to be scaled down to an appropriate size. It was like looking through the wrong end of a telescope.

My arrival at camp was greeted, for once, by excellent news. My release had come through. Queen's University had petitioned for my return as a temporary assistant lecturer and I could now join Gwyneth, who had been on the Queen's staff for eight months. The aircraft carrier *Indefatigable* was currently loading troops for demobilisation. I joined her at Colombo and home we sailed. Effectively my war was over. On the whole, I wouldn't have missed it.

The Beckoning Ghosts

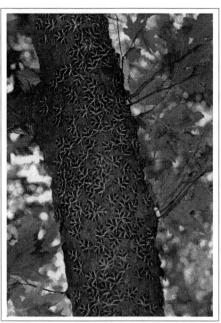

Jersey tiger-moths on a tree trunk, Petaloudes,
Rhodes (Photograph courtesy of Michael E. Arfaras)

This piece of narrative is really a total hotchpotch of utterly trivial events which have somehow resisted the passage of years and stayed vividly in my mind. I suppose most of them could be tied in with the reasons I became a biologist in the first place and remained hooked on the fascination of the natural world. Certainly neither my genes nor cultural background are likely to be responsible, since none of my ancestors were biologically, or even scientifically, orientated. The one possible exception would have been my paternal grandfather, who took a degree in civil engineering in Heidelberg University over 120 years ago. Moving to South America, his main achievement was to design the drainage system of Buenos Aires. Never having visited that city, however, I cannot comment on how his work might have affected, say, the town's urban ecology. I just hope his drains are still doing their job.

Throughout a youth plagued in early teens by an obscure and long-lasting viral infection which wrecked any formal schooling, I never wanted to be a doctor, fireman or train-driver – though the idea of becoming a distinguished racing motorist had a fleeting attraction. I did pass through various natural history enthusiasms – birds' eggs (before their acquisition held criminal connotations), African antelopes, moths and fresh-water insects. As regards the last, I became a helper, at the age of eleven, to Professor Gregg Wilson, then lately retired from the Zoology Department of Queen's, who was working on the distribution and abundance of potentially dangerous mosquito species in the Belfast area. He was a small, kindly Scot with a rich accent and was impeccably dressed for our pond-trawling expeditions in a smart dark suit and trilby hat. When we reached our pond he would cautiously glance around before stripping for action. His jacket was now revealed to be lined by many little pockets from which dangled an array of small soup ladles, forceps, hand lenses, miniature nets and other collecting gear. The ladles could be screwed on to his walking stick and specimen tubes emerged from a holder stitched inside his hat. Within a minute, this respectable Presbyterian pedestrian was transformed into a fully equipped, academic naturalist who had somehow strayed from the Victorian era. Oddly enough, his hunt for mosquitoes held a special interest for me. I knew and admired the story of Sir Ronald Ross and his research on malarial mosquitoes and this had a personal connection since on our junior school football team I played alongside Ross's grandson.

Up to the age of eight, I lived at the end of a secluded lane near the southern edge of Belfast. From our garden a shallow valley sloped eastward, one side occupied by old allotments, the other flanked by a hay meadow grazed by a few cattle and bordered by some ancient fir trees. Tiny streams trickled down towards a small lake. Early on summer mornings, when the sun flooded into the meadow, the air was filled with the calling of corncrakes. Although less than a mile from the centre of a large city, this old field was a favourite breeding spot. Alas, it is now many years since that raucous chorus could last have been heard. My father used to curse the corncrakes for awakening him so early and swear that he would take his gun and shoot them – but he never did. It seemed amazing to me that the voices of these same unseen birds would, in our winter, echo across the countryside of southern Africa.

Holidays were a good source of fleeting but unforgettable experiences. Once, on a sheltered and deserted beach in north Antrim, I watched a big roller build as it neared the shore. The newly risen sun shone through its advancing crest, creating a long parapet of clear green water. Abruptly the wave was disturbed by the entry of a dolphin straight in front of me. The great spindle shape smoothly accelerated, running swiftly along the moving wave for many yards until the roller broke into glimmering foam. As the animal vanished, I found I was breathless, shocked by a sense of primitive excitement. Many years later, in the Cocos lagoon, something rather similar happened. A couple of hundred yards from our fourteen-foot boat, what appeared to be twelve huge fins rose periodically above the surface before changing course to head straight for us. Then they vanished, to reappear dramatically a few seconds later beneath the boat in twenty feet of translucent green water. They were six enormous manta rays measuring over fifteen feet in width from tip to tip of their fins. As they passed underneath us, the illusion that they were fly-ing was complete. These monstrous fish, swooping so close on their vast wings seemed like alien but beneficent invaders from a mythical world. I was utterly awestruck.

For a couple of summers in the mid-thirties we lived in the shadow of the Mourne mountains, about half a mile from a famous landmark, the Bloody Bridge, scene of a tribal massacre in 1641. Here the Mournes really do 'sweep down to the sea' and are fronted only by small meadows which collapse into steep glens ending on a rock-strewn narrow beach. In high summer these glens were magic, their streams peopled by an extraordinary number of large dragonflies which hunted up and down the slope. Out to sea, gannets dropped and plunged like white, elegantly carved arrowheads to fish the abundant swarms below. The rough pastures inland, soaked in the scent of gorse, were by day alive with meadow-brown and wall butterflies, but at dusk a new world awoke. I would wander these slopes with my cousin Rosemary, who had similar gypsy leanings to the outdoor life. As the daylight dropped and the overarching mountain became a great black wall, these meadows held two soft but dominant

A male Ghost Swift moth with brilliantly white wings rests on a grass head.

sounds. With a low drone, large dor beetles blundered through the dusk, while nightjars churred and clicked as they hunted moths. Occasionally a slumbering horse would awake with a startled snort and canter off into the darkness. The really haunting denizens, however, were the ghost swift moths. The large yellow and brown females were almost invisible as they dropped their eggs at random on the grass, but the males were spectacular performers with gleaming, almost luminescent white wings, which carried them in side-to-side swinging flight.

Over the years, one of my main interests has been the ways in which animal species form associations of various sorts with each other. Perhaps those dor beetles, droning away in the bewitching twilights of County Down, played some part in triggering this addictive interest. Digging them out from their chosen feeding places (large, messy patches of cow dung) their polished cleanliness seemed remarkable. But their undersurfaces almost invariably revealed a small cluster of tiny mites clinging tenaciously to

———— ∞ ————

them and providing a highly effective cleaning service by eating dung fragments.

An interspecies association with a more personal slant involved me some years ago during a holiday on the Croatian coast. Since my return from war service, I had been periodically afflicted by mild outbreaks of the well-known fungal disease athlete's foot, which led to areas of infection between the toes. The warm Balkan climate had caused another outburst and one day, after a swim, I sat on a rock and let my legs dangle in the water, thinking that a saline soak might alleviate the painful itch. It did – but for altogether different reasons. Becoming conscious of a tingling sensation, I looked down into the clear water and saw a party of little shrimps busily working on my toes. They moved around purposefully, nibbling away at the tender patches. After several minutes they wandered off – and I had no more trouble with athlete's foot. Like the professionals they were, they had completely cleaned it up. For a number of years we had known that various species of shrimp and fish specialised in these cleaning activities, freeing other members of the marine fauna of parasites, growths and infected wounds, but this was the first time I had personally (and gratefully) experienced it.

It was on this same trip that I fell in love with the town of Dubrovnik. Like my child-haunted village in Sri Lanka, it seemed perfectly proportioned on a miniature scale. Its charm was increased by flocks of the big brown alpine swifts screaming loudly as they swept at breakneck speed above the tiny streets, over the squares and around the battlements and ancient walls. And it was on a dusty road outside Dubrovnik that I partially caught up with one of my boyhood ambitions. During my moth-collecting days, the hawk-moth family especially enthralled me. Mostly large and streamlined, they are everything a moth should be. Of these noble insects, my favourite was the oleander hawk. This could measure five inches from wing-tip to wing-tip and its colours were shades of olive-green with pale grey areas and lines of pink and beige, all elegantly blended. It was first recorded in

Britain in 1833 by a lady who found it in her drawing room in Brighton, but has always remained exceedingly rare since it

is, in fact, native to Africa. My ambition to find it was kept alive by the fact that occasional individuals were reported from widespread localities in the British Isles. Two were even noted (one in 1938, the other in 1954) within fairly easy

Oleander hawk-moth. Scale = 1 inch (adapted from The Moths of the British Isles, by Richard South. Published by Frederick Warne & Co. Ltd.)

distance of my own home. Its caterpillars feed principally on oleander and periwinkle. This is an interesting selection of food plants, since the former is highly toxic to humans, while the latter has now been discovered to have many therapeutic properties. However, to revert to my walk along that small Croatian road, I spotted something lying by the edge. It was a detached forewing of my ideal moth. I picked it up as if it was the Holy Grail itself. Even a single wing was better than nothing.

We had a much more spectacular encounter with moths on the island of Rhodes some years later. Amongst its tourist attractions, Rhodes boasts a 'Valley of the Butterflies'. This valley, Petaloudes, is about six miles from the northwest coast and the 'butterflies' are, in fact, moths. They belong to the tiger-moth family and the one in question we call the Jersey tiger (*Panaxia quadripunctaria*). The Germans call it the Russian bear – why, I have no idea. It spans about two inches and is vividly coloured, with dark brown forewings crossed by cream stripes and red hindwings with several large black spots. Although common enough in the Channel Islands, it is a scarce moth on the south coast of Britain.

In Rhodes, however, the Jersey tiger has some remarkably strange habits. The moth occurs in a number of places throughout the island where the females lay their eggs. But in June and July, these egg-laying habitats become deserted as every individual migrates to the little valley of Petaloudes. This is an area of rough country with ravines clothed in large trees and shrubs and where little streams trickle around rocks and boulders. This immigration takes place only at night and each individual flies there alone – there is no group flight. Walking through the valley is an impressive experience, for the Jersey tigers are there in thousands, sitting on leaves, plastering the rock-faces, occasionally fluttering slowly to a different spot. At the end of June, all moths in the lower part of the valley move towards its upper reaches, thus concentrating the population still further. There is also evidence of sexual preferences – males tend to settle near ground level, while females adopt perches higher up, many of them in trees. In September, *Panaxia* copulates in the Petaloudes valley and afterwards returns to the egg-laying habitats elsewhere on the island. You may recall those wonderful mythical yarns about elephant graveyards

A swarm of Jersey tiger-moths clustering on rocks at Petaloudes, Rhodes. (Photograph courtesy of Michael E Arfaras)

in Africa, to which all aged and infirm elephants are said to move in their last days. Although at Petaloudes, reproduction rather than death is the prevailing theme, it might seem a similarly climactic place for the Jersey tiger. Ecologically speaking, there must be something very special about this particular region for these lovely moths. Probably the numerous streams and abundant vegetation provide a uniquely favourable, humid and shaded environment. It is also just conceivable that the presence of many sweetgum trees (*Liquidambar orientalis*) which secrete a golden, vanilla-scented resin could perhaps trigger biochemically the moths' mating behaviour.

Remembering *Panaxia* en masse brings me back to one of the earliest biological observations Gwyneth and I ever made. Almost sixty years ago we climbed a heath-clad slope beside Cave

Hill, a small peak overlooking north Belfast. We had a large, newly emerged female emperor moth, a species well known for its ability to attract mates from some distance. It was April and a cool wind blew over a deserted moorland. The female obligingly extruded her scent organs from the tip of the abdomen and moved them rhythmically. Within a minute or two several males, ranging upwind, found her. To be honest, I was rather surprised. Doubt had been cast on the presumption that the males follow a scent by the opinion of the celebrated nineteenth century naturalist J.H. Fabre, who remarked that it would be as reasonable to expect a single drop of carmine to tint a whole lake. Nevertheless, we now know that scent is widely used for mate finding in the insect world and in many other animal groups as well. The really astonishing feature is the hyperacuity of the male moth's detection system, located principally in its feathery antennae.

Rhodes was not the only Mediterranean island to furnish a piece of memorable biology. We were staying in a small hotel chalet on a Sardinian beach and had been adopted by a friendly domestic cat that wandered in and out of our quarters. After returning from a swim, we found it drowsing on the verandah. Suddenly something emerged from its fur, moved rapidly over its back and vanished. After several reappearances we realised what the intruder was. There is a curious family of dipteran (two-winged) flies called the Hippoboscidae. Although in every technical sense true flies, most of them have wings of reduced size and a few no wings at all. Their flying periods are usually very limited, but since they have powerful hooks on their feet, they are speedy and efficient runners. Some live as external parasites (ecto-parasites) among the feathers of birds – the swift, for example, is frequently infected – while others are found amongst the fur of mammals. Our Sardinian cat was clearly a host to a hippoboscid species. As we knew the Zoology Department had no specimen of this intriguing group, we were determined to capture it. After filling a small specimen tube with gin (the only alcohol to hand), we made our initial move by gently cuddling the cat. But however swiftly we swooped when the fly made its erratic appearances in the fur, it was clearly the master of the situation. After twenty minutes, we decided that our quarry would have to be isolated in a limited patch of fur. We took the cat – now getting somewhat hostile – into the bathroom and ran a shallow bath of tepid water. Bending over to hold the cat, while leaving a hand free to pounce, irritated our friend even more. There was nothing else for it – we climbed in and joined the cat in the bath. With the three of us flailing around, a chaotic minute followed until the fly finally surrendered. Thank goodness there were no other guests in adjacent chalets at the time. Our fly now occupies a special microscope slide in the parasitology section and has been carefully drawn by several generations of students. The manner of its capture has also passed into legend.

Just north of Sardinia lies Napoleon's island of Corsica and I remember some wonderful dusks in a ravine enclosing the town of Porto on the west coast. The town buildings are clustered on the northern slope, while across a narrow arm of sea to the south rises an enormous forest of chestnut trees. As the summer night drew on, the trees blended into a great dark mass reaching skyward. From somewhere out of this blackness drifted the song of a nightingale. As the liquid melody trickled across the gap another bird joined in, then more and more added their voices to the chorus. Within a few minutes, the night was awash with the lovely, confident music. Inevitably, it brought Keats' ode to mind. I knew now something of what he had felt in that far off twilight at Hampstead – and he was listening to one bird only!

My first serious research at Queen's was a survey of the floating life of Strangford Lough at its narrowest point – the half-mile width of the Narrows between Portaferry and Strangford village. Since the lough is nineteen miles long, the race of water through the Narrows with each spring tide is very rapid, reaching about eight knots. Our hauls with a large plankton net were usually taken at slack water – that short period between the turn of the tides. Even in a haul lasting only a few minutes, the net concentrates the number of tiny animals and plants, so that under a low power microscope the water is like a living soup. It is easy then to understand how the plankton is the basic food of the sea, with nearly all marine life ultimately depending on its presence.

The most striking feature of planktonic animals is their amazing variety. Many marine invertebrates of all sorts have young stages which live in this 'floating' zone, often sinking by day and swimming upwards at night. Both larvae and adults may sport bizarre shapes and may also incorporate so much water in their bodies as to become transparent to the point of virtual invisibility. Both of these features greatly retard their rate of sinking, so that little energy need be expended on swimming. Show any bored marine student a jar of apparently clear sea water and tell him animals, an inch long, are swimming in it and he will be hooked for life. A planktonic worm called *Tomopteris* and the so-called arrow worm (*Sagitta*) can only be detected because their swimming movements create water currents.

Another fascinating aspect is the ability of some planktonic animals to produce light (bioluminescence). This is "cold" light – very efficient when compared to, say, an electric bulb, in which much energy is wasted in the production of heat. Generally speaking, two substances are necessary to produce this light. One is called *luciferin* whilst the other, *luciferase*, is an enzyme which interacts with *luciferin* in the presence of oxygen. Sometimes the light is confined to luminescent organs, which may be quite elaborate and may include a lens. In other cases, a luminescent cloud is extruded into the sea. Rowing a boat after dark will often result in bursts of light as the oars disturb the water and much of this luminescence may be due to the presence of large numbers of a tiny single-celled organism called *Noctiluca*.

This phenomenon, however, is not confined to planktonic animals, but occurs widely throughout the marine world. Burrowing into sandy mud around Britain is the long-armed brittle star, *Acrocnida brachiata* – an animal which, for me, holds some pleasant memories. These stemmed from a collecting trip in 1963, when we dug a few specimens near the mouth of Strangford. Up to fifty years ago only seven brittle star species, out of the 1800 species then described, were positively known to produce light – and this very small list did not include *Acrocnida*. On our marine course that year we had an assistant who was collecting and preserving fresh specimens for the depart-

A group of long-armed brittle stars (Acrocnida brachiata) *in burrows on the sea bed. Each individual has extended some of its arms in a search for small particles of food.* (Photograph courtesy of Bernard Picton)

ment. She worked in a tiny improvised darkroom in the cellars of the marine station and word reached me one evening that she wanted to see me at once. Anne was not only an intelligent and friendly girl – she was also stunningly good-looking. Nothing loath to join her, I hurried downstairs. By the light of a single dimmed bulb, she was poised over a white dish containing an *Acrocnida* in an inch of water. With some effort, I transferred my attention from Anne to the brittle star. "I was trying to relax it with a solution of propylene phenoxetol" she explained, "when suddenly it lit up." "Let's try it again" I said. Sure enough, we got a brilliant display of luminescence, emanating from the lateral surfaces of the arms. The bright, bluish-white light lasted for only a few seconds and

With Anne, who first noticed bioluminescence in the brittle star Acrocnida, *1963.*

repeated stimulation seemed to exhaust the animal's capacity to respond.

Well, it's always nice to discover something new and this simple example should reassure any young, pessimistic marine biologist that there are, in fact, many aspects of marine life about which we know virtually nothing. So take heart – the information is somewhere out there, waiting for you. What really struck me about the *Acrocnida* episode was that this brittle star was first made known a long time ago. It is not particularly small and occurs in many places around British and European coastlines. Yet although an enormous amount of marine research has taken place over the past couple of centuries, no one (apart from the gorgeous Anne) had ever noticed its behaviour if stimulated after dark, since Montague first described *Acrocnida* in 1804.

Of course, a few other things also happened in 1804: John Keats had his ninth birthday; the younger Mr Pitt was once again elected prime minister of England – and Napoleon Bonaparte proclaimed himself Emperor of France.

Spanish Treasure and an Enigmatic Animal

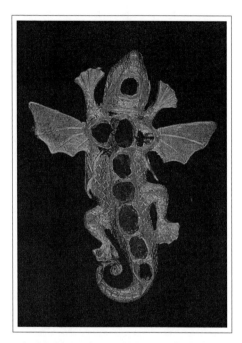

The "Golden Salamander", a small pendant from the wreck of the Spanish galleass Girona.
(By kind permission of the Trustees of the National Museums and Galleries of Northern Ireland)

In 1967, the northeast coast of Ireland suddenly became a focus of intense interest to marine archaeologists. This hinged on the discovery and excavation of a wreck near the celebrated Giant's Causeway in County Antrim. The wreck was no undistinguished merchantman which had foundered on this rugged coast, but a well-documented ship of the Spanish Armada. You

——— ∞ ———

may remember that after the rout of this great fleet, the surviving ships fled the ensuing storm in a desperate bid to return home. They dispersed widely, several clawing their way up the west coast of Ireland, perhaps in an attempt to repair and refit in the less hostile waters of Scotland. After putting in at Killybegs in County Donegal, one galleass pushed further north to round the tip of Ireland before encountering another great storm and driving helplessly on to the waiting rocks. Although its ultimate fate was well known, the actual wreck was not discovered until 1967, despite the fact that the general site had been called for many years *Port na Spaniagh.*

To make a long story short, the resulting treasure haul was bought by the Ulster Museum. The exhibit which perhaps created the most interest was a little model of an animal quickly christened 'the golden salamander'. To sustain the wave of public interest engendered by this intriguing find, I was asked to contribute a short article in a local newspaper, dealing with salamanders in a general sense. On handling the model, however, one thing became abundantly clear: our 'salamander' had so far escaped the eye of a zoologist!

My account, which originally appeared in November 1972, is essentially as follows.

"On a night in late October, 1588, the Spanish galleass Girona foundered on the inhospitable rocks of the North Antrim coast and with her perished more than 1,300 survivors of the ill-starred Armada. The story is now as well known as its sequel – the discovery, 379 years later, of her wreck by Robert Stenuit, and the ingenious, patient salvaging of many interesting objects.

Of these items, now superbly displayed in the Ulster Museum, one in particular possesses a certain zoological interest in addition to its great intrinsic beauty. This is the little gold model of a newt-like creature, inset with jewels and adorned with small wings, which has come to be known as the 'golden salamander'.

Salamanders are, of course, amphibians related to our own

newts and, somewhat more distantly, to the frogs and toads. Though not native to the British Isles, their startling black and yellow colouration make them familiar as decorative, if rather unemotional, 'pets' in vivaria.

Given the accurately salamandrine proportions of the Girona animal, plus the fact that these amphibians, then and now, would be common enough in the Spanish countryside, it is not unnatural that the little gold model should have been described as a salamander. I believe, however, that such an interpretation is wrong, and that the forgotten goldsmith who created this masterpiece was inspired by an altogether different animal, more remote and exotic by far. The reasons underlying this assertion are as follows.

Salamanders, like almost all other amphibians, possess a smooth and completely scaleless skin. The model, however, is clearly provided with scales – an obvious reptilian feature.

Next, the arm of a salamander has only four fingers – a rudimentary fifth digit is present, but does not appear at the surface. The Girona specimen on the contrary, has a five-fingered hand – again, a reptilian character. Finally there are those wings! Was this a mere decorative whim on the part of the craftsman – a little gold left over, perhaps, or possibly something of heraldic significance? These are certainly tenable theories, but do not, on balance, seem to me very probable. Moreover, if we look at the flanks of the animal, we can see that the goldsmith has carefully modelled what are clearly the infolded remnants of a further wing-like expanse. What on earth was the man about?

It looks as if we are forced to conclude that what the artist was striving to reproduce was based on a real lizard-like animal, possessed (however improbably) of winged expansions along its flanks. Does such an animal in fact exist, and would the Spaniards of the 16th century have known about it?

The answers to these two questions are, respectively, 'yes' and 'almost certainly'. From India eastwards through Malaysia and the island chain of the East Indies there occurs a genus of small lizards known as flying dragons. The scientific name of the best-known species, *Draco volans*, is a literal translation of the popular term. Quite a number of species have been described, differing from each other only in minor details. They are mostly tree-dwelling forms, living on ants and other insects, but what makes them

zoologically fascinating is their capacity for gliding flight and the manner in which this is achieved. Along each side the skin is expanded into a thin membrane, supported and stiffened by greatly lengthened extensions of the animal's posterior ribs. Thus equipped, these lizards can make gliding leaps to lower branches up to 30 yards distant. When not in use, the 'wings' are folded into a series of pleats along the sides of the body.

The flying dragons reach the eastern extremity of their geographical range on the Philippine islands, first made known to Western Europe by Ferdinand Magellan in 1525. Various Spanish expeditions visited the group in subsequent years, and the first permanent settlement was established there in 1565, some 23 years before the Armada sailed against England.

Flying dragon, a lizard - and the probable model for the "golden salamander" of the Armada treasure.

It would appear inconceivable that an animal so bizarre and paradoxical as a 'flying lizard' would not have been shipped many times to the Spanish homeland as a curiosity by the new colonists. Might it not have been such a specimen, probably dried and mummified, which gave our goldsmith his inspiration? Indeed a mummified example would largely account for the admitted anomalies in this interpretation.

A dried condition would certainly explain a tear in the fragile wings, leaving part of the membrane folded – a feature, as I have said, faithfully reproduced by the modeller. If the lizard's already slender body appeared unduly shrunken, the craftsman might also (with justifiable artistic license) have felt obliged to fill it out a little until he considered it to be life-like, thus producing the heavier and more familiar salamander form. On the other hand, this may simply have been an attempt to produce an ornament that would be somewhat more robust.

A final point of some slight academic interest may be mentioned. The first scientifically recognised description of the flying dragon is that of the great Swedish systematist Carl Linneaus in 1758, and it was he who christened the genus *Draco*. But perhaps we may now consider that in a sense Linneaus was subtly forestalled by a matter of two centuries. For it would surely seem that an earlier, more romantic version has lain hidden in the waters of the North Channel – a description not in the medium of the printed word, but through the silent eloquence of Spanish gold."

Although this story may have sustained some public interest, I began to get the feeling that my contribution (or rather my interpretation of what had now become a hallmark of the exhibition) was not entirely welcome. Iconoclastic theories seldom are, since they disturb established, cosy explanations. We shall probably never know precisely what had served as a model for this exotic little ornament, which seemed to have been originally designed as a pendant. At the time it was first exhibited, political events in Ulster had escalated into unimaginably violent tragedies. Perhaps the greatest irony is that the political/religious horrors, which for the next 30 years engulfed the Province, were so weirdly identical to those ancient emotions which precipitated the Armada adventure itself. After a gap of four centuries, this small enigmatic beast had dramatically emerged to link these episodes of bitter, bloody history.

The Human Element
Professors, Players and Partners

After a practice. Irish Davis Cup team v. Great Britain at Devonshire Park, Eastbourne, 1969. From left: Ken Reid, me, Peter Jackson and Michael Hickey

If you're keen on fancy dress and circus parades, academic life could well be your cup of tea. Several times a year you may put on an anachronistic gown and unreal headgear and shamble untidily along with fellow addicts to graduations or other university rituals. Please don't get me wrong on this: I approve unreservedly of tradition and I like celebrations – but as an onlooker only. Similarly, if you enjoy arguing about almost anything, any number of university committees are eager to enrol you and facilitate this whim. Again, I have no objection to argument per se – but don't expect me to join in. I have enough blood-pressure problems as it is.

Thanks to these spineless inclinations, my career in the university was distinctly low key. I quite liked teaching and tried to help my students in any way I could. I loved research even though it entailed all those legendary frustrations and dead-ends which are familiar to every scientist. To such handicaps was added a strong sense of isolation, since, in those early days, no one in the British Isles was specialising in my particular neck of the woods. In this post-war era we were also perennially short of research funds.

Despite my lack of involvement in traditional university affairs, my attitudes were probably influenced by a number of the senior academics I encountered. Frederick Ogilvie was the first Vice-Chancellor I met – but only because his son, at the age of ten, was a casual boyhood friend. I remember him as a kindly if rather aloof man who did, however, achieve some fleeting fame when he left Queen's to become Director General of the BBC. These were the days when all the signs indicated that a second world war was in the immediate offing. Ogilvie, who evidently believed in the efficacy of subliminal psychology and who knew (like everyone else) of Hitler's passion for Wagner, forbade any broadcasting of that composer's more martial themes. Unhappily, this admitted attempt to discourage the dictator did not prevent the invasion of Poland a few months later. How Sir Frederick would have reacted in the subsequent decades of Ulster's troubles, in which party songs and noisy bands were of keynote significance, is any-body's guess.

When I returned to the university after serving in the Air Force, the Vice Chancellor was David Lindsay Keir. He was tall, dark, undeniably handsome and possessed a very genuine but almost overpowering charm. To encounter him, however casually, was to trigger a return to the courtesies of 16th century England. If women were involved, he didn't exactly make a formal bow, but the downward sweep of his hat and outstretched arm came pretty close to it. These invariable and rather touching gestures made him a master of fund-raising for Queen's. He also had the envi-able ability to get along splendidly with everybody.

Of course, his well-meant urbanities occasionally misfired. At that time, relatively small numbers of academic staff – usually about thirty – were invited to tea parties in the Vice-Chancellor's Lodge. Just how one was selected to attend these agreeable occasions (known to the irreverent as 'Servants' Balls') was never disclosed, but it was considered only decent to accept. Although not short of hired help, the Vice-Chancellor was clearly delighted to have the chance of serving his guests personally. "Do have some cake, Mrs Gotto" he coaxed Gwyneth, who was sitting in a low armchair. He inclined gracefully from the waist, proffering a large sandwich cake, smothered in castor sugar, towards her immaculately groomed lap. Conscious that Grecian drama was still alive and well, I watched with fascination as the slippery cake tilted inexorably towards the edge of its plate to cascade in a cloud of sugar on to her skirt. Lindsay was appalled – but, as with any consummate performer, quickly recovered.

His successor was Sir Eric Ashby and if ever an exceptional financial administrator followed a gifted fund-raiser, Ashby was certainly that man. He was a distinguished botanical researcher and it was comforting to know that a biologist was in the right spot to stimulate work in the life sciences. He helped me by communicating one of my early papers on a new copepod species to the Linnean Society – and I never held it against him that he once tried to dissuade me from playing any more competitive tennis. This was based on his flattering but erroneous assumption that since Wimbledon winners such as Lew Hoad were known to put in six hours practice per day, I, as an Irish international, must be making the same inroads on the university's time.

Of the professors I knew at Queen's, I have already mentioned Theodore Thomson Flynn, father of Errol. Although his main research centred on the embryology of marsupial mammals, he also worked on sea fisheries, fossil whales and the marine invertebrates known as sea spiders, as well as leading the Australian Antarctic Expedition of 1912. Just before he retired from the Zoology chair at Queen's, he shrewdly embarked on a year's sabbatical leave, roaming the Caribbean with Errol in the latter's schooner, the *Zaca*. Reappearing briefly in the university, he produced photos of the trip. The crew seemed to include a fair number of entrancing film starlets who clustered protectively around Errol and his father. Although the voyage was technically scientific, I imagine Theo, God bless him, enjoyed himself thoroughly.

Occasionally, he would expand on the subject of his world famous son. "When Errol next comes to Belfast, you must play tennis with him" he said. "He's a pretty good player." In fact, Errol had performed well as an Australian junior player. "When he plays on a hard court" Theo told me "the blood pours from the back of his right hand." "How's that Prof?" I asked. I knew a lot about tennis elbow – but this! "Well, you see" said Theo "he gets down to the ball so well on the backhand that his knuckles scrape the court!" After that, of course, I couldn't wait to play this masochist – preferably for a modest bet. Unfortunately the match never materialised – Errol died a few years later and was followed by his father in 1968 at the age of 84. Incidentally, Errol had a sister, Rosemary, whom I remember partnering at a university dance. Before you enquire, Errol was the sole inheritor of the stunning good looks known the world over, but Rosemary was a very pleasant and agreeable girl to take to a dance.

My botany professor was Jimmy Small, a Scotsman and a remarkable academic of a type now virtually extinct, who could cross the boundaries of his own science and make a significant contribution in some unrelated field. He had once written to the government's air transport authorities connecting (in some way I have forgotten) the stomatal opening mechanism in plants with such major airship disasters as the R101. In particular, he eventually developed what might be described as a statistical approach to the interpretation of evolutionary method (QE, or quantitative evolution) which, in some respects, foreshadowed and paralleled the recent and widely accepted evolutionary concept now known as punctuated equilibrium. He also became one of the university's most notable characters. Beneath a forbidding, almost malevolent exterior, there lurked a splendid vein of pawky, sardonic humour. He had a long-running feud with medical students who, in their first year, were obliged to study botany. The origin of this alleged hostility was said to lie in an epic confrontation in the adjacent Botanic Gardens, which left the professor struggling out of a lily pond. I always got on well with Jimmy, partly because we were both interested in techniques for taking photographs of small, living objects – in his case plants, in mine, moths – and we used to compare prints.

I must mention Professor Stewart of the Chemistry Department, since I came to regard him as The Man Who Came Close To Saving My Life. A major casualty of the first World War and a subsequent survivor of almost every ailment known to man, one of his greatest achievements was, quite simply, his continued existence. Profoundly deaf, he carried a box strapped to his chest which was fitted with various switches and a quite large movable funnel into which, on invitation, one spoke. His visual state necessitated enormous pebble-lens glasses and his vivid complexion suggested major cardiac and respiratory problems. Another legacy of his war service was a distinctive, robotic walk with short, jerky steps. When he lectured to first year students, he could only be heard by the front row, since chaos reigned throughout the rest of the theatre. Sublimely unaware of any disturbance, he trundled on for the statutory fifty minutes.

My momentous encounter with him came at the end of the first year practical exam. I knew almost nothing about chemistry (never having studied it before university), but had learnt a few rule-of-thumb tricks in qualitative analysis. I had eliminated our unknown exam substance down to a dubious choice of three, but was then totally ignorant of any further enlightening procedures. With one minute to go, I had started to sweat profusely, envisaging a further year in this hellhole of incomprehension. At that moment the Prof, inspecting the exam's closing stage, paused behind me. "Well, my boy" he said, adjusting his funnel and throwing switches, "and how are you getting on?"

"Quite well, Professor" I lied. "I've analysed it down to three substances so far." He held my notebook to his nose while he read my choices.

"Well", he grunted, "it's hardly likely to be *this* one or *this* one" – and trotted off. If I had not been paralytic with relief, I would have run after him, dropped to my knees and clasped his shins like a devotee of Mahatma Gandhi.

Stewart's other achievement was to be the author of highly rated and very widely read detective novels in the 1930s, under the pen name of J. J. Connington. They were masterpieces of logical analysis, the plot frequently hinging on detailed knowledge of railway timetables and other such minutiae. They also abounded in phraseology even then anachronistic, bouncing the reader back into, at latest, the Edwardian era – "By Jove, this is a rum go!" – and similar exclamations. Perhaps because of all these eccentricities, I remember him with affection and, needless to say, gratitude.

Academic life demanded some diversion and I had started to play tennis again. The wartime gap had, of course, put paid to any chance there might have been of carving a career out of the game and in any case I now had, with luck, a permanent job. But I trained hard and put together enough performances to be an accepted entry for the Men's Singles at Wimbledon in 1949. Indeed, there was one memorable day in June of that year when I learned, in the space of 12 hours, that I had gained my MSc degree, had landed the first lectureship in the Zoology Department to be awarded in ten years and had been accepted to play Wimbledon.

In action at the Championships, Wimbledon in 1957

I may as well expand a little about tennis, since it became quite a major facet in my life. In 1953, having won the Irish Open Hard Court singles and doubles titles, I was selected for the Irish Davis Cup team to play Finland in Helsinki. In that era, there

THE HUMAN ELEMENT – PROFESSORS, PLAYERS AND PARTNERS

were usually two Irish players who were deservedly automatic selections and since, for economic reasons, an Irish travelling team generally consisted of only three players, it came down to a strenuous fight for the third berth. By dint of playing endless trial matches year after year, I managed to hold on to my place until 1961, when we played Poland in Dublin. In that year I became forty and had reached the stage when the possibility of playing a five set single at Davis Cup level was becoming

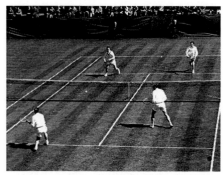

My last Davis Cup doubles v Poland, Fitzwilliam Club, Dublin, 1961. In the far court, Joe Hackett (left) and I in play against Skonecki (left) and Gasiorek

slightly intimidating. I therefore retired but acted as team captain for a few more years, which entailed some more pleasant, if nerve-racking trips to the Continent.

I suppose the appetite for competitive sport must have been deeply embedded in my genes. My father was a fine golfer and a good tennis player, but his main sport was hockey, which he quit at an early stage before I was born. He made his debut for Ireland at the age of seventeen and as centre forward put together some spectacular performances. At that time it was within the rules to bounce the ball on your stick and as Dad had a low grip plus an excellent eye and sense of balance, he could weave his way at speed through an international defence before grounding the ball deep in the circle and slamming home a goal. At Abergavenny on one occasion he scored seven goals in thirteen minutes against Wales – which I imagine is still a record. One of his brothers was capped for Ireland at rugby. On the other side of the family, my mother's brother also played international rugby and her father had, at one time, held the Irish 400 metre record. The genes concerned were apparently still active, since our son David, on taking up squash at the ripe age of twenty-one, was playing for Ireland four years later and went on to become the world's most internationally capped squash player, representing Ireland 122 times.

Although tennis was becoming very popular in the early fifties, Northern Ireland was not a good environment in which to improve. The climate was too fickle to guarantee uninterrupted outdoor play and there was a total absence of indoor courts. Grass courts, already rare, were mostly of poor quality. In Ireland generally, our grass seems ideal for breeding top class racehorses, but not good for tennis players. Many of the hard courts (mostly clay) were advanced in years and provided an uncertain surface. Visits of competent professional coaches were extremely rare, although there was no shortage of enthusiastic amateurs who could tell you how to play every shot. Among these remote control experts were two of my elderly uncles who would appear in the front row when I was playing a local tournament. They never sat together but parked themselves at opposite ends of the court. I remember battling against a Czech Davis Cup player in the semi-final of an Ulster championship. Although no world-beater, he was a very useful full-time performer and I was struggling to hold him. One of my problems was all too audible avuncular support. If I ventured close to the stop-netting at one end there would be a loud, attention-seeking hiss from Uncle Bertie. "Play to his forehand, you fool – he's got no bloody forehand!" At the other end of the court, Uncle Louis was present to keep me right. "Hit to his backhand, for God's sake – he hasn't got one!" These were lapses of my opponent's technique that I had certainly failed to spot. I need hardly add that I lost the match, but it was sufficiently close to satisfy family honour. My father, thank God, never gave me any trouble. He would sit beside Gwyneth and be ecstatic if I won a lengthy rally and consumed by despair if I didn't. But, as always, Gwyneth stood in for me, absorbing both parental elation and doom with admirable stoicism.

Playing at Wimbledon five times between 1949 and 1959

and other international matches were bonuses for all the sweat and effort, since they occasionally allowed you to gauge yourself against some of the world's best players. Until late in the 1960s, when tennis shed its amateur status and became open, the leading performers in major tournaments were in fact playing for money, although often holding nominal jobs. Full-time play against their peers inevitably created a gap in standard which was almost impossible to bridge for the rest of us. Among the Wimbledon winners I remember playing were Victor Seixas, Tony Trabert, Budge Patty, Jaroslav Drobny, Ashley Cooper, Neale Fraser and Jean Borotra. Of these, Borotra was perhaps the most interesting for a variety of reasons. Born in Biarritz in 1898, he became one of the famous 'Musketeers' who held the Davis Cup for France over six consecutive years. He played in five Wimbledon Singles finals, winning two of them, and his last Davis Cup match came when he was 49. At 51 he was still good enough to win the British Covered Court singles for the eleventh time. This was remarkable testimony to the amazing agility that he had managed to retain, since a wood court ensures a lightning fast surface.

Jean had been an heroic figure to me since I was eight. This was largely because I had discovered a picture of him, complete with his habitual black beret, plunging across a court to illustrate the word 'volley' in my children's encyclopaedia. I didn't play him, however, until he was 59. In Dublin to attend an international tennis conference, he had been persuaded to enter the men's doubles in the Irish Championships. Amid a stack of other preconditions, he insisted on being partnered by a good young player, so the committee paired him with our junior champion aged 18. The search then began for gentlemanly opposition unlikely to offend the visiting legend. After some judicious draw-fixing, the choice fell on Cyril Kemp and myself – both well past our best with a combined age of 80. Although we won in straight sets, the match was no pushover, since the large crowd had fallen wholeheartedly for the charisma which Borotra exuded. This was even more apparent some ten years later when James McArdle and I met Borotra in the second round of the Veterans' doubles at Wimbledon – an event limited to players over the age of 45. On this occasion, another former Davis Cup man, Bernard Destremau, his junior by nineteen years, partnered Jean.

At Wimbledon, Borotra's charm and magnetism had always been abundantly evident. On whatever court he played, a significant proportion of the gallery consisted of old men with panama hats and waxed moustaches and elderly ladies with flowery hats and often in wheelchairs. James and I won a somewhat nervy encounter in which we were unmistakably cast as the baddies – but the fun was not quite over. James was chatting to a relation some fifteen yards away when we were collecting our towels and rackets to leave the court. An old lady leaned over the canvas:

"Monsieur Borotra" she said, "may I ask how old you are?"

Borotra seized her hand and kissed it. "Dear lady," he said, "I have 69 years." Gasps of amazement all round.

"And I," said Destremau, getting into the act, "am 50."

They then turned on me. "And you," they enquired, "how old are you?"

"I am 47," I replied.

"There you are," said Borotra to his fans. "He is a child – no wonder we lose. And your partner, how old is he?" James was 48, but I was becoming tired of this endless analysis, which was obviously destined to discredit us in the end.

"James?" I said. "You'll not believe this, but he is 83 – and it costs a fortune to keep him fit." This outrageous statement effectively terminated the discussion.

At the end of the war, Borotra went through a rough period. After the German occupation he had accepted a job as a sports minister from the Vichy régime, which implied some degree of collaboration with the puppet government. In the circumstances, it was difficult to see what else he could have done and in fact future events fully vindicated him.

Another of my former opponents also had a tough war. Hans

Redl had played for Austria in 1937 and for Germany in '38 and '39. He had been swept up into the German army and had lost his left arm in the siege of Stalingrad. He took up the game again in 1946 – but had to throw the ball up from his racket face when he was serving. The rules of lawn tennis were subsequently amended in order to make Redl's serve legitimate. I can vouch for the fact that he had a pretty good delivery and for one suffering a major disablement, he was in fact a remarkably graceful hitter of the ball. Although impeccably behaved in a single, he could be devastatingly sarcastic to his partner in a double and it was quite apparent that the whole Austrian tennis establishment was terrified of him. Poor Hans! – I reckon he had every excuse for his frustrations on court.

Mixed doubles never had quite the same macho image as other events and major tournaments, then as now, offered few examples of husband and wife teams. However, I recall one couple that stayed in my mind largely because their history provided such dramatic contrasts. In the late 1940s an Argentinian pair, Heraldo and Maria Weiss toured the world circuit. He was remarkably handsome, lean and tanned and a highly athletic player. I played him once and was struck by the enormous amount of spin he could impart to the ball. Maria was classically beautiful in a Hispanic way and played with intelligence and power. They were close friends of Juan and Eva Perón and certainly had no financial problems. During the Ulster Championships in Belfast, the Argentinian president and his wife were confronting one of their recurring political crises and the telephone line to Buenos Aires was in constant use as the Weiss's anxiously contacted the Perón establishment. This caused some consternation to the tournament committee, who were going to be landed with the phone bill. However, the crisis was apparently overcome and the couple resumed their charmed existence.

The next time I saw Heraldo, he was sitting close to me in the competitors' stand at Wimbledon. He was clearly not absorbed in the centre court match. The tan was still there but the features

——— ∞ ———

were haunted and the eyes anxious. After a few minutes he left. Some months later I heard he was dead. I lost track of Maria, though her name surfaced a few times in tennis contexts. Then silence, until I read, quite by chance, a small news paragraph which told me she had fallen from a high window. Although I barely knew them, I remembered their earlier, carefree existence in the tennis world and momentarily felt a sense of almost personal loss.

A remarkable performer at Wimbledon in the early fifties was the American player Arthur Larsen. Slightly built and with a somewhat dishevelled air, Art was a supreme magician on the tennis court. Not endowed with overwhelming power, he could nevertheless use every shot in the book to out-think the opposition. In 1950 he was number one in the United States and eventually reached number three in the World Rankings. Women were clearly fascinated by him and it was rare to see him unaccompanied by a small group of attractive girls. A large part of his public appeal, however, lay in his behavioural eccentricities. These had developed following a horrifying experience in the world war when serving in the US army. Trapped in a blazing tank, he was the sole survivor of a miraculous escape. This improbable deliverance left him unbelievably superstitious, expressed in all sorts of compulsive rituals. Between rallies he had spells when he would elaborately step over the lines of the court rather than walk on them. On changeovers he would carefully tap the net post, umpire's chair or any other object in reach, thus giving rise to his popular nickname Tappy Larsen. Above all, he would glance repeatedly over his right shoulder. He explained this by saying he was checking that his eagle was still perching there. This tame eagle (invisible to the rest of the world) would sit on his shoulder during a match. If it flew off, his game would deteriorate. Art's career came to a rather tragic end in 1956 when he was badly injured in a motorcycle accident.

I suppose the most notable (or notorious) Irish player of my era was George Lyttleton Rogers, though in fact we didn't quite overlap and I never played him. George was 6' 7" and possessed a formidable serve. He turned professional before the war but regained his amateur status a few years later. During his professional spell, he played a series of 19 head-to-head matches against the legendary Californian Don Budge. In city after city Budge triumphed and the tour was nearly finished when, in their seventeenth encounter, Rogers finally won. As an American tennis magazine put it, this win surprised everyone – except Rogers, who maintained airily that after all, "class would tell in the end!"

George was a great prima donna who would, on occasion, lock his bedroom door on a Davis Cup trip and tell his team captain that he didn't feel like practising today. One of his partners told me that George's ideal situation in a Davis Cup tie was for him to win his two singles and his partner to lose both of his, so that in the vital doubles match, George could "pull him through in the end", thus becoming the hero of the hour.

H.H. The Sultan of Pahang - probably the owner of the world's largest tennis shorts - partnered by me, playing at the Windsor Tennis Club, Belfast, 1959

Although internationals in many sports can produce long lists of celebrated acquaintances, such was not my fate. I did play tennis with the Sultan of Pahang (a genuine tennis fanatic and the possessor of the most voluminous shorts I have ever seen) and had brief conversations with the Duke of Luxembourg, Charlton Heston and Eamon de Valera – but that's about it. I also had one memorable encounter at Wimbledon. Watching the closing stages of a match, I suddenly remembered that I was due to occupy that same court when the current match ended. I made a dash for the changing room a hundred yards distant and hurled myself at the inner door. There was resistance, then a startled gasp as some emerging body fell to the floor. I picked him up and dusted him down, apologising profusely. "Entirely my fault" he said, which was patently untrue, while I wondered why his face was familiar. My victim was Clement Attlee, then Prime Minister. He was so pleasant and reassuring that I was almost tempted to vote Labour at the next election.

I am sometimes asked how the top flight players who were around in my earlier years would have fared against the world-class performers of today. I believe the answer is simple, but the causes are not always obvious. The old-timers would lose and probably rather badly. However, this does not mean that they were innately less talented than their successors. The first thing to remember is that the game itself has altered significantly (though, interestingly, the dimensions of the court have not). The massive injection of money over the past 30 to 40 years, through television, sponsorship, endorsements, etc has induced more people to seek their livelihood on the court either as players or ex-players who have become coaches. Great advances in specialised training methods, knowledge of nutritional needs and much improved physiotherapy enable players now to cope better with a continuous programme of match play.

In many ways the game has also become easier. The tie-break system has eliminated those enormously protracted and potentially exhausting sets in which one sometimes became involved. The provision of seats at the umpire's chair and the ninety second rest allowed when players change ends only became legal in the 1970's. Prior to that, if you lingered for more than ten seconds, you could be accused of stalling. The foot fault rule, enabling the server to leap forward, enhances the importance of possessing a powerful delivery. Above all, the present day rackets are very different from the beautifully laminated wooden frames of yesteryear which weighed between 13 and 16 ounces. Nowadays, the racket face can be considerably larger – but the racket weight can be as little as 8 ounces. Because the frame is made of "space-age" material and is very rigid, the chance of developing arm-strain with so light a racket is minimal. Stringing has altered too, allowing a much greater range of tension.

These are the main reasons why the leading players of today can hit the ball harder and generally with a great deal of spin. However, from the 1920s on, I can think of at least ten players who could probably hold their own against the moderns, with the important proviso that they had today's equipment and experience in using it.

Did I ever try to blend the two activities in which I became absorbed – marine biology and international tennis? The answer is yes, if only to a limited extent. Trips to the Continent for Davis Cup matches occasionally allowed time to contact zoology departments in local universities – often the start of useful correspondence. In the Netherlands I could visit a long-time friend and colleague, Jan Stock, whose field of research in parasitic copepods was almost identical to mine. Jan held a Chair at Amsterdam University and was an incredibly productive worker, writing over 120 papers on copepods alone. A fertile imagination was allied to a highly developed sense of deadpan humour and he invented some fascinating items regarding his own life. Many of us were convinced, for example, that he had been born in some romantic spot in the East Indies – but Amsterdam was in fact his birth-place. Jan died in 1997 and I lost a great friend and endlessly entertaining companion.

Party in Nanaimo, British Columbia, 1997. From left: myself, Bob Kabata, Gwyneth, first cousin Rosemary and Mrs Mary Kabata

While on the subject of eminent copepodologists, I must mention another good friend, whose life really has included many dramatic events. Zbigniew Kabata (known as Bob) was born in Poland and was fifteen when his country was invaded in 1939. Survival in Warsaw and clandestine work for the resistance movement was followed by a perilous escape through Europe and, finally, sanctuary in Britain. He joined the Free Polish Forces and was trained in Scotland as a machine-gunner, eventually going through the north African campaign. At the end of the war, unable for political reasons to return home, he headed back to Scotland and took a job on a Scottish trawler in Aberdeen. At first, he told me, he became interested in the fish and then in the parasitic copepods which infested them. The Government gave him a grant to Aberdeen University, thus launching a career of dedicated brilliance. Although now officially retired, he continues to work at the Canadian government's Pacific Biological Station. He is the world's leading authority on the copepods parasitic on fish with an immense list of publications. Some years ago he persuaded me to co-author a synopsis of parasitic copepods in British and west European waters. Our combined efforts proved too large for a single volume, so separate books eventually appeared in 1993.

I will close this rambling account by relating a curious coincidence where my two worlds – tennis and copepods – really did melt into each other. My last work on *Mychophilus roseus*, the little red sausage which so obsessed me, was written in conjunction with Mark Holmes and Peter Lowther. The latter was the son of an old tennis friend and I had supervised his honours degree at Queen's, part of which consisted of a scanning electron microscope study of the male *Mychophilus*. Peter went on to take up tennis as a career and, like myself some twenty years earlier, played on the Irish Davis Cup team. Since Ireland first entered this competition in 1923, only seventy men had represented the country up to 1999 – a very small group. A great deal smaller was the number of people in Ireland who had seriously researched parasitic copepods – at most, perhaps, a dozen. Because of this coincidence, I had begun to think of the 1984 paper on Mychophilus as "the Davis Cup paper". I mentioned this recently to our third author, Mark Holmes of the National Museum of Ireland. He agreed it was certainly curious before adding the absolutely clinching remark: "You know, Viv" he said, "one of my uncles also played internationally." Somehow, coincidence had skipped a generation – but I was left with a peculiarly uncanny feeling.

The Problem Solvers: A World of Houdinis

Leptosynapta inhaerens

Our conception of space, literally in a universal sense, has profoundly altered over the past half century. Those rocket-powered vehicles, which Gwyneth and I successfully dodged in London so long ago, pointed the way to escaping gravity and tiptoeing to the edge of the unexplored. Over the same period there have been endless speculations as to the possibilities of other life forms, but these have not been confined to outer space. Increasingly refined methods for investigating the sea and in particular its abyssal depths, have led to many remarkable discoveries. Here I want to say something about the mysterious beasts I know best – the little copepod crustaceans that live with other marine animals.

These small creatures have no popular names and their very existence, let alone details of their biology, is known only to a small handful of marine biologists. However, they share our world and their amazing, often incredible lives are perhaps worth a passing glance.

Although the sea is full of copepods swimming around freely, those species which rely on the presence of host animals often have very precise requirements which can only be met in extraordinarily specialised ways. Let's take an extreme example. Some years ago, a friend, Brian Jones, then of New Zealand Fisheries, trawled up some waterlogged wood off the New Zealand coast from a depth of around 4,600 feet. The wood was being eaten by what proved to be a new species of deep-sea limpet. Attached firmly to the limpet was a copepod, subsequently christened by Brian *Cocculinika myzorama*. It consisted of two parts – a series of tubes embedded in the limpet's tissue (through which

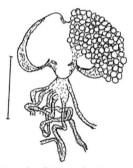

it presumably nourishes itself) and an outer, heart-shaped portion less than 2mm wide. Two sheets of its eggs were wrapped closely around the parasite. There were no traces of any appendages whatsoever.

So here we have a copepod specialised to such an extent that it has lost every vestige of feelers, mouthparts and legs. In its life cycle it must rely on finding a highly adapted limpet, itself compelled to seek out sunken driftwood, in a depth of water which would comfortably submerge Ben Nevis! Here is

Female of Cocculinika myzorama *showing one egg sac and the nutritive tubes normally embedded in the tissue of its limpet host. Scale = 2mm*

a world of permanent darkness, icy temperature and enormous pressure. Yet *Cocculinika* survives, finds a mate and completes its life history. This copepod has been put together by a set of genes specifically capable of achieving this improbable result. Talk about doing things the hard way!

You may have wondered, when dealing with an animal so devoid of recognisable features as *Cocculinika*, how we know that it is in fact a copepod, or even a crustacean? The answer lies largely in the presence of paired egg sacs, which nearly all copepods possess. However profoundly the body has been moulded by the demands of evolution, twin egg sacs provide a major key to copepodan identity. Should the eggs hatch, you would have further proof, since the structure of the first young stage – called a nauplius larva – furnishes more clues to its identity as a member of the copepod group.

When I started research over fifty years ago, only a small number of copepods were known to live as permanent partners of other marine invertebrates. For obvious economic reasons, the species which parasitised fish were much better known. At first, I investigated mainly those which lived with sea squirts and in an earlier chapter I told of my attempts to unravel the mysteries of *Mychophilus*, the little red sausage from *Botryllus*.

Living inside a sea squirt has many advantages for a copepod which seeks a quiet stress-free life. Not many predators attack sea squirts which, as items of food, are rather unrewarding. This alone makes them desirable hosts for a variety of specialised copepods. The chief difficulty, however, in studying the biology of their associates is, quite simply, that you can't peep inside most sea squirts. The outer wall (tunic) is usually too opaque to permit a view of the copepod. However, a patient search of Strangford Lough happily produced an answer.

A group of sea squirts (Corella parallelogramma) *showing extreme transparency of the outer body wall.* (Photograph courtesy of Bernard Picton)

Quite often, our dredge hauls would include a beautiful sea squirt called *Corella parallelogramma*. It is fairly large, reaching a length of about two inches and is strikingly coloured, but its main feature is the glass-like transparency of its outer coat. You can easily make out almost all of its internal organs. Moreover, it is among the many hosts which are inhabited by a large copepod, *Ascidicola rosea* – a name freely translatable as 'the rosy-coloured dweller in the sea squirt'.

Let me very briefly introduce *Corella* in a little more detail, since sea squirts may not be familiar to many readers. Imagine a conical glass flask, glued by its broad base to the seabed. The flask's mouth allows a stream of water to flow in. Nearby is a second hole through which waste water can flow out. Most of the flask's internal space is occupied by a large, delicate 'cage' (actually the pharynx, part of the animal's food canal). The 'cage' is thinly covered on its inner surface by a sheet of mucus, as if it had been wallpapered. However, this wallpaper is moving! Propelled by the rhythmic beating of many microscopic 'hairs' (*cilia*), the sheet travels slowly around the cage until it reaches a ridge at one side. By now it has picked up a mass of minute floating life from the inflowing water and, at the ridge, it congeals into a food-laden string which is slowly drawn into a compact stomach. This in turn leads to an intestine which opens close to the outlet hole. The latter exit also gets rid of the filtered water, plus the sea squirt's waste material and reproductive cells.

Diagram of a simple sea squirt to show how it filters and concentrates minute food particles. Arrows show direction of water flow. T=sieving tentacles, P=pharynx ("cage"), F=food string, S=stomach, I=intestine, A=anus, W=outer body wall

Having transported my copepod-infested *Corella* to the university, along with carboys of seawater, I was faced with a new difficulty. Our rooms and laboratories were centrally heated and, at that stage, we had no cold room. However, the Department included a little pseudo-Gothic tower and its top room was vacant. This was not surprising as it had lost most of its window panes and had never been reached by the central heating system. It was, therefore, freezing and windblown to boot – a perfect haven for my cold-loving sea squirts. It was reached by a decrepit spiral staircase and it was in this abandoned garret that I set up shop.

In order to monitor as many copepods as possible in their living hosts, I improvised half a dozen of that primitive viewing aid known as a camera obscura. I 'borrowed' the low-power (x10) lenses from ancient unused microscopes and made ground-glass screens from exposed photographic quarter plates. Each lens and screen, secured by plasticene, was housed in a cardboard cylinder. Infected *Corella* were propped up in individual glass tanks filled with sea water, with an electric lamp placed behind each tank in line with the lens. This arrangement provided an enlarged silhouette of the sea squirt's internal structure and of the four millimetre-long copepod living there.

After dark, I would visit the empty Department and negotiate the treacherous spiral up to my windy little attic in the tower, feeling rather like the Lady of Shalott. During the night the Department was peaceful and my viewing arrangements were perfect in the prevailing darkness. In many ways, it was a very satisfying piece of research. Moving at leisure from one screen to another, I could view the behaviour of *Ascidicola* in all its aspects and realise that this was probably the first time that a living copepod had been seen going about its business inside an undisturbed host. The ground-glass screens also made possible some rather crude photography, using an old triple extension camera which I had bought some years previously for £7. If a print (shown here) of *Ascidicola* looks like an early x-ray, it should be remembered that the shot was taken through the body wall of the host, a couple of inches of sea water and the wall of a glass tank.

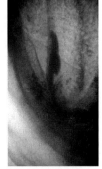

Photo of female copepod Ascidicola rosea *living within its sea squirt host* Corella

One of the first answers to emerge concerned the location of *Ascidicola* within *Corella*. Previously, we had thought of such copepods as grazing over the mucus sheet at random and simply removing trapped food particles. This, however, was not the case. The copepod's position was in the oesophagus, a little curved part of the food canal which links the pharynx with the stomach. The food string, an encrusted rope of mucus, passes through the oesophagus and it is to this that *Ascidicola* clings. Since the food string is slowly drawn downwards towards the stomach, the copepod maintains its position by climbing up the string. It was a little like watching someone toiling up a descending escalator.

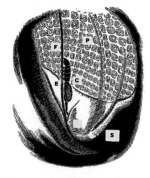

*Interpretive drawing of C=*Ascidicola, *head end towards the top of the picture, P=pharynx ("cage") of sea squirt, E=oesophagus, S=stomach, F=food-string of mucus and concentrated food particles to which* Ascidicola *clings*

To spend your life clinging to a string on which your food is conveniently concentrated is evidently better than wandering over a carpet looking for crumbs. That *Ascidicola* has been successfully doing this for millions of years is clear when we look at its structure in more detail, for it is a superbly equipped rope climber. The body is long and narrow, rather than bulky; many of the bristles (setae) on its legs are very long and possess tiny hooks which engage with the mucus string to provide a secure hold and finally there is a little pad of spiny tissue near the end of the body which acts very like the crampon of a mountaineer.

Sometimes the food string becomes thin and wispy, forcing the sea squirt to reduce its feeding activities. When this happens, *Ascidicola* may tug at the mucus cord with a vigorous movement of the head as if to say "come on, you're slacking!". If the host stops feeding altogether, the copepod may turn through 180° and clutch the last remnants of the passing string before it vanishes into the squirt's stomach. On the other hand, a string very heavily laden with entrapped particles often seems too much for the guest to handle. On these occasions, *Ascidicola* will lie cradled and motionless in the curve of the oesophagus, resembling a satisfied gourmet asleep in a hammock.

Perhaps the most interesting problem to be solved concerned the reproductive strategy of *Ascidicola*. Its pink eggs lie in two thin oval masses protected by long plate-like extensions, which are, in fact, the copepod's modified fifth legs. An egg mass may consist of anything between 20 and 70 eggs. Each egg is enclosed in a bubble-like, clear membrane and these in turn are clustered together within a common outer membrane. The question was simply this: How did the eggs or the newly hatched larvae (*nauplii*) get out of *Corella*? If released from their protective membranes, they might exit either through the mouth of the pharynx (which would mean battling against a strong inhalant current) or pass through the rest of the host's alimentary canal already packed with food products. The trick is to evacuate these tiny vulnerable stages safely from a host which is, after all, specifically designed to capture and eat micro-organisms.

One night, as I watched the screens in my cold retreat, a female left her position on the food string and entered the opaque stomach. When she returned to the oesophagus some minutes later, her egg masses had vanished and a new batch of eggs was being laid. Fascinated, I concentrated now on the host's intestine and presently several eggs, each still protected by its transparent bubble, appeared from the stomach and slowly travelled up the intestine towards the anus. A batch of about 30 eggs took half an hour to cover the last 8mm of the food canal. As they left the anus, they encountered the full strength of the outflowing current. The inner membrane was explosively ruptured and the newly hatched young shot out of the exit hole at high speed. For the next six days they would have to take their chance as feebly swimming midgets in the ocean currents.

From these sessions I would walk the half mile home well after midnight, with the silhouettes of the copepod's slow motion activities burnt into my eyeballs. With each discovery I marvelled at the complex perfection of adaptation and timing. The final explosive escape of the nauplii from their potentially lethal host seemed especially impressive. But every time I scaled my spiral staircase, I wondered what new magic would be revealed.

The peacock worm (Sabella penicillus) with its filaments extended. (Photograph courtesy of Bernard Picton)

It was shortly after the *Ascidicola* research that I became involved with a very different copepod. Across the lough from our Portaferry base lies Castleward bay, a shallow, calm stretch with a floor of mud and fine gravel. Here and there it is populated by peacock worms (*Sabella penicillus*), elegant and beautiful, which build narrow tubes of fine mud anchored in the sea bed and projecting about a foot into the water. The worm's head is crowned by a fan about four inches across composed of rather stiff filaments. In undisturbed conditions, this fan spreads out from the mouth of the tube and filters minute food particles from the water. Any touch (however slight), a vibration in the water, or even a passing shadow will cause the fan to be rolled up and withdrawn into the tube at lightning speed. If you wade very slowly into the water and then remain motionless, the worms will presently extend their fans and give an excellent impression of small brownish-pink palm trees sprouting around your feet.

Four egg bearing females of the copepod Sabelliphilus elongatus *clinging to the filaments of its worm host. Each copepod is about 1.5mm in length.*

In 1862, a Norwegian biologist, Michael Sars, discovered a copepod, *Sabelliphilus elongatus*, which lived with the peacock worm and is found nowhere else. Less than 2mm long, it clings tightly to the fan's filaments. Since the fan is the worm's food-gathering organ, it was natural to assume that *Sabelliphilus* filched a fraction of its partner's food as it was passing slowly towards the worm's mouth – in other words it was considered a commensal or non-paying guest. Only more detailed scrutiny revealed that it was, in fact, a committed parasite.

Each food-gathering filament has a groove along the inner surface which is lined by mucus-secreting cells and cilia – tiny 'hairs' which beat rhythmically towards the host's mouth. Very small particles trapped by the mucus are conveyed by the cilia along the groove to be engulfed by *Sabella*. However, the copepods invariably cling to the upper surface of the filament and so are remote from the food-gathering mechanism. This upper part is smooth and rounded and is grasped by the large antennae of *Sabelliphilus*. The antennae are marvellously fashioned into a locking device, fitting snugly around the filament's curve and are clamped on to it by several powerful claws.

Interpretive drawing of the copepod Sabelliphilus elongates

A very noticeable feature was the alignment of *Sabelliphilus* along the filament. Every copepod was orientated with its head towards the filament's base. As many as eighteen copepods could occur on the worm's fan – and not one out of step! Furthermore, if copepods are released into a dish containing nothing but severed filaments arranged at random they will settle on these fragments the 'right' way round. Clearly this is a vital part of their behaviour pattern.

The reason for such precise alignment was, for once, immediately obvious. The great speed and vigour with which the worm withdraws its fan into the shelter of the tube imposes the absolute necessity of being firmly locked to the filament and maintaining a perfect streamline to counter the abrupt shock of the withdrawal reflex. To adopt any other orientation would be fatal – the copepod would be swept away by the sudden fierce movement and would probably have its two trailing egg sacs sheared off by the mouth of the host's tube. Once lodged, *Sabelliphilus* maintains its position for long periods, though it will occasionally scuttle quickly to a new site along the filament's length.

That this little copepod is an ectoparasite can be demonstrated if we carefully remove one from its established site – not an easy task as it clings really tenaciously to the filament. But its point of attachment is often marked by a slight erosion of the worm's tissue, indicating that *Sabelliphilus* is actually nibbling away at its host. It also shows a distinct preference for settling its head on the narrow bands of darker pigment which occur at regular intervals along the filament. These areas probably represent the richest source of food, but *Sabelliphilus* enjoys a snack of worm mucus as well. All in all, we may regard it as an exceptionally well adapted parasite.

The surface of a female Eunicicola. *Details are omitted except for the large sucking disc which is flanked by the antennae. Each antenna carries two minute suckers on the terminal segment. Scale=0.5mm*

I once had a brief opportunity to drop in on the life of another fascinating copepod, *Eunicicola insolens*, which also partnered a marine worm. In 1961, we were dredging in the Irish Sea close to the entrance of Strangford Lough. In a depth of 40 metres the dredge brought up a large membranous tube which housed an active reddish coloured worm, *Eunice harassii*, about 12 cm long. Comb-like, bright red gills decorated each body segment. This impressive worm was host to 31 tiny copepods, less than a millimetre in length, but with classic copepodan proportions. They had only been reported three times since they were first described in 1877 and their general biology was virtually unknown. To find so many live specimens was therefore a considerable bonus.

These little associates glided smoothly over the body of their large partner, sometimes disappearing into the groove between successive segments. They also moved very actively over the blood-filled gills. Attempts to dislodge them, using the tip of a fine needle, were not successful. *Eunicicola* lacks any grapnel-like claws or hooks, so close adhesion to the host is achieved in an altogether different way. On the copepod's undersurface, close to the mouth, is a large sucking disc. Under the microscope, it looks absurdly similar to the rubber sucker which tips a child's toy arrow – though it is functionally far more efficient. But when *Eunicicola* clings to the gills, this large sucker can be of little help, since it is too broad to create an effective vacuum on the slender gill branches. However, the copepod then plays a different card. Each antenna has two slightly bent bristles (setae) near its tip and each ends in a very small sucker. In life, the antennae are extremely mobile, performing both flicking and circular movements with equal ease. The minute sucking discs have no difficulty in clamping on to the gill branches even when these sway vigorously as the worm moves.

The use of suckers is not, of course, restricted to *Eunicicola*. They are present on a number of other copepods and are used as adhesive devices quite widely in the animal kingdom. The fish known as shark suckers or remoras have transformed certain fins into sucking discs and that primitive curiosity the lamprey has one around its mouth. Leeches and many other invertebrates also possess suckers. In fact, as American showman P. T. Barnum said (admittedly in a different context): "There's one born every minute."

So far, I have only mentioned research which was fairly easy to set up and carry out. I will now recall one effort which really did become something of a nightmare. Strangford is home to several species of burrowing sea-cucumbers – elongated, worm-like relatives of starfish and sea urchins. They are a few inches long and the head end is crowned by a circlet of small branching tentacles which shovel sand, mud and debris into the mouth. Some of these cucumbers are hosts to copepods belonging to the genus *Synaptiphilus*. On the French coastline, they are generally 'paired up' in a nice, organised fashion – one species of host to one species of copepod. But in Strangford the choices are fewer. We have only one species of copepod, *Synaptiphilus tridens* which occurs on two species of cucumber – *Leptosynapta inhaerens* and *Labidoplax media.*

Synaptiphilus, less than a millimetre long, lives on the cucumber's skin. This skin is very rough, due to the presence of tiny, sharp barbs and if you pick up a sea-cucumber with your fingers, it is quite difficult to disentangle it from your own epidermis. The copepod's tenacious grip on its host is maintained by sharp, spiny hooks on the base of its feelers (antennules) which engage with the cucumber's skin. In whatever conditions you keep the host (cold or warm temperatures, light or darkness) the copepod will tend to position itself on the anterior third of the cucumber's body, although it is perfectly capable of running rapidly to a different location.

Female Synaptiphilus tridens carrying two egg sacs. Scale=0.5mm

The skin of *Leptosynapta* is also rich in mucus glands of two sorts, one secreting an acid mucus and the other either a mucoprotein or neutral mucus from a narrow region just behind the tentacles. Since the copepods seem to live mainly on these secretions, they can thus dine á la carte. The discriminating gourmets among them evidently prefer mucoprotein, resulting in most *Synaptiphilus* positioning themselves immediately behind the tentacles.

In Strangford, the shallow burrows of *Leptosynapta* are plentiful in a sheltered inlet, Ballyhenry bay. Here the sea floor is very mixed – mud, sand, small gravel, shell debris, weed etc – and the copepod is present on about 20% of the cucumbers. Close to the entrance of the lough, four miles south of Ballyhenry, lies Kilclief bay, a uniformly sandy area where *Leptosynapta* is very sparsely infected by its copepod partner. Kilclief is much less sheltered than Ballyhenry, so I assumed at first that colonisation by *Synaptiphilus* was just too difficult under the prevailing, wilder conditions found there. However, to make sure that both populations of *Leptosynapta* did in fact belong to the same species, I sent samples to Georges Cherbonnier in Paris, who was an expert on the group. He assured me that both samples were indeed *Leptosynapta inhaerens*, but was surprised that it was inhabiting the very mixed substrate at Ballyhenry. Apparently its French cousins would never have dreamed of living in such a place!

It was at this point that the whole affair became much more complicated. In the laboratory, if we transferred *Leptosynapta* from Ballyhenry to the relatively clean sand of Kilclief, our cucumbers enthusiastically burrowed down as if the summer holidays had arrived. But if specimens from Kilclief were introduced to the coarse substrate of Ballyhenry, many became sluggish, lost their healthy pink complexions and even began to die off. They were, in short, not happy cucumbers.

*The head and front part of the body of a sea-cucumber (*Leptosynapta inhaerens*) showing the feeding tentacles. (Photograph courtesy of Bernard Picton)*

A colleague Andrew Ferguson, suggested we carry out some electrophoretic trials on the two populations. Electrophoresis, in brief, is a biochemical technique which separates out proteins and is now widely used to help determine relationships between species in evolutionary studies. The results were surprising. The degree of difference between *Leptosynapta* from Ballyhenry and those from Kilclief suggested that, physiologically, these apparently identical animals might almost have belonged to two different genera, let alone species.

I rather wish I had left it at that. But I became haunted by the notion that what happens in a laboratory is not necessarily identical to what might take place in the wild. We noticed a strong tendency for copepods from Ballyhenry hosts to abandon a Kilclief *Leptosynapta* within two to five days. But what would happen if the new (Kilclief) host was in its natural environment on the shore at Kilclief?

If you, too, are obsessive, you can readily see where this was going to lead me! I found myself isolating a *Synaptiphilus* from a Ballyhenry cucumber, placing it on the skin of a Kilclief host, filling a two gallon plastic bucket with Kilclief sand and then driving 30 miles to Kilclief. Sometimes this had to be done at night to catch the low tide. I would stumble across the dark shore carrying my bucket and spade, dig the bucket well into the sand and drive back to Belfast. A fortnight later I would return to retrieve it and painstakingly sieve through the sand to find the cucumber. Frequently I would conclude that all this was a ludicrous expenditure of time and effort – and I have no doubt that *Leptosynapta* and *Synaptiphilus* thought the same.

The net result of all these endeavours was a tentative conclusion that one form or genotype of *Leptosynapta* was better adapted to the Ballyhenry substrate and environment, but could also survive on Kilclief's sandy shore. A second genotype might be virtually restricted to Kilclief. These genetic differences could also include the production of slightly different mucoid secretions. We only had one instance of a transferred copepod surviving for long (thirteen days) on a Kilclief host. Since it seemed that only 'Ballyhenry-type' mucus was a suitable diet for *Synaptiphilus tridens*, this one exception could be explained on the assumption that its host happened to be a 'Ballyhenry' genotype, rare at Kilclief.

On the whole, this was a frustrating piece of work. Indeed, it only qualifies for mention in this essay because it highlights one notable feature in host-parasite relations: that individual hosts may differ in subtle but important respects which may challenge the adaptive ingenuity of the parasite. Adaptation, in short, is not necessarily a one way street.

Back in the 1860s, a strange looking copepod was found in a large sea squirt at Brest on the coast of Brittany. Its describer was Eugene Hesse, a French engineer attached to the Department of Marine Administration. He collected copepods exhaustively along the Biscayan coast, from Brest and Lorient in the north to Bordeaux in the south. For over two decades he contributed notes and observations on a variety of copepods associated with marine invertebrates. His descriptions were often highly confusing and his illustrations frequently grotesque. Present day researchers, seeing his name appended to a species, are apt to feel a distinct frisson of apprehension. Yet despite this, Hesse is regarded with almost affectionate tolerance. No one can doubt his enthusiasm for his hobby (which perhaps led to some banter in the local seaports) and his drawings were occasionally accurate enough to identify an obscure copepod to at least generic level. The copepod cited here is a case in point.

Having, as usual, no common name, we must fall back on its scientific one, *Notopterophorus papilio*. This translates as 'the butterfly-like one, with wings on its back'. At most, the body is about 3mm long and looks like a normal, if somewhat elongated, copepod. But what has befallen its upper surface? Here the skin has been drawn out and developed into six enormous wing-like expansions which hide the rest of the body. The copepod can't swim, but it can (very slowly) gently flap these vast, filmy 'wings' so that, under a low power microscope, a group of these amazing

Notopterophorus papilio
female lying on its back, with the tail end at the bottom. The very large filmy "wings" sprout from its upper surface. This copepod is about 3mm long.

animals rather resemble slow motion dancers enveloped in large transparent veils.

As can be imagined, the function of these extraordinary wings evoked considerable speculation for over a hundred years. Hesse himself had the idea that they might aid *Notopterophorus* in its slow movements within the sea squirt's pharynx, which is the only site occupied. The British copepod specialist of his day, George Brady, considered them far too delicate for such a function, adding, in a somewhat defeatist vein, "we must, I think, admit that their use is at present quite unknown". Other ideas, however, were quickly forthcoming. Some biologists thought that they might act in a gill-like manner, their large, thin surface aiding oxygen uptake. Others considered they might originally have developed as fat storage organs and still others wondered if their purpose was to protect the eggs before hatching. Finally, Isaac Thompson of Liverpool, clearly impatient with all this guesswork, concluded: "It is difficult to imagine any use to the animal of the extraordinary appendages ... so much resembling in general appearance the wings of a butterfly".

This, then, was the situation up to the middle fifties, when we found *Notopterophorus papilio* in about 15% of individuals of a large species of sea squirt in Wreck bay, Strangford. This little inlet had long been a dumping ground for ancient vessels awaiting break-up, notably one which had been towed back from France, where it had acted as a block-ship during the Allied invasion. It was near its shattered keel that we found our squirts. I had been intrigued by the wings of *N. papilio* for years and now enlisted the help of my colleague, Lawrence Threadgold, in an attempt to find out exactly what their purpose was. Lawrence's involvement was vital, since he was an excellent cell specialist who could perhaps unravel the wings' finer details by electron microscopy.

Did we solve this long standing problem? That's hard to answer – but at least we put forward a reasonable theory based on more intimate knowledge of the wings' structure than had hitherto been possible. A significant part of our explanation hinged on details of biophysics and biochemistry which, I must admit, still make my head spin. In this brief account, therefore, I will not burden you unduly with these aspects, but will simply summarise our conclusions.

———— ✀ ————

At the start of this chapter you may remember the problem faced by *Ascidicola* – how its tiny young had to be safely evacuated from the sinister confines of a sea squirt's gut? Well, *Notopterophorus* faces the same dilemma, but is unable to solve it, as *Ascidicola* does, by sneaking into the host's stomach to deposit its eggs. Encumbered by the large, trailing wings, the female is not designed to squeeze into the stomach and in any case its eggs hatch into little swimming larvae the moment they leave the mother's body. The only option for the female is to shed her young into the pharynx and hope that they will be able to exit through the 'mouth'. Can she achieve this feat against the inflowing current? If not, her brood is doomed to be trapped and eaten by the sea squirt.

Scattered over the wings' surface we found many elaborate little sensory structures which were clearly designed to monitor the microenvironment close to the copepod. For various reasons, we believe they are particularly concerned with detecting minute changes in water pressure and current flow. It is only by being 'aware' of alterations in these factors that the female copepod can safely hazard the release of her helpless young from the inherent perils of their nursery – and the timing must be perfect.

I stress this accuracy in timing since it is apparently linked to a momentary, fleeting reaction on the part of the host. Sea squirts are well known to "back flush" – that is, spontaneously squirt water out of their mouths – hence, indeed, their popular name. This only happens occasionally during the squirt's feeding cycle and is of very brief duration. It is presumably a useful way of eliminating particles unsuitable as food, but it will also take place if the inside rim of the mouth or a circlet of oral tentacles guarding the pharynx are gently stimulated. During a back flush, the outlet opening of the squirt closes while the mouth remains open to allow the violent ejection of water from the pharynx.

These reactions will obviously cause changes in current flow and hydrostatic pressure within the sea squirt. It seems probable that such changes can be monitored by the sensory receptors on the surface of the wings, inducing the female to move towards the mouth region and ultimately trigger the back flush reflex which will sweep the hatching young safely out of the host.

Why are the wings so large and elaborate in copepods of this type? If indeed they act as a test-bed for sensory monitoring it may be advantageous to have the sense organs scattered over a wide area. But there may also be another reason for their spectacular development. You probably remember those horrific stories of explosions in aircraft at high altitude, in which unfortunate travellers are literally sucked through a hole in the damaged plane. Only those wearing very bulky clothing are saved, simply because they are too large to be ejected. It may be that when the squirt's back flush is triggered, the female copepod is prevented from being evicted for much the same reason and thus remains in the host to produce her next batch of eggs. Once again, we are seeing an extraordinarily complex interplay between copepod and host.

Living in association with another animal often demands remarkable manipulations of both structure and sexual activities. Of course, if the partnership is a fairly loose one, everything proceeds much as would be expected. Males are usually smaller and more mobile than females since they must actively seek out the appropriate host and locate a receptive female. But for sedentary, often immobile females, we find frequent examples of the male sex being ingeniously transformed in totally unexpected ways. Sometimes they have been transmuted into tiny, grotesque dwarfs which spend their lives clinging to their large bloated partner, often, conveniently, beside her genital opening. The end point in this line of evolutionary specialisation is reached when a larval male invades the female and then proceeds to reduce his body until all that is left is virtually a mass of sperms. This final result bears a deceptive resemblance to hermaphroditism.

Can sexual anomalies surprise us still further? Indeed they can. *Pachypygus*, a close relation of *Notopterophorus* but lacking 'wings', inhabits large sea squirts in Strangford. Its magic act is to have two sorts of male – one a small, active swimmer which can enter and leave the sea squirt at will and the other significantly larger but only capable of crawling within the host's pharynx. The larval stages from which they develop are identical until they have gained access to the host. If the latter is very young and still untenanted, the invader is destined to become a swimming male. If the host is more mature and, in particular, if it is already housing a female copepod, the new arrival will develop into a crawling male. In such cases, therefore, sex is not solely a simple matter of genetics but is, ultimately, determined by environmental factors. Sexual ethics in the world of copepods would greatly excite our human moralists!

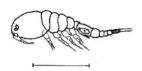

An atypical (swimming) male of Pachypygus.

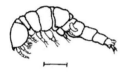

A typical (crawling) male of Pachypygus. Scale = 0.5mm

It's said that involvement with miracles constitutes a powerful claim towards achieving sainthood. Over the past half century, the copepods have exposed me to undreamt of marvels. I have been bombarded by the extraordinary, drenched by the totally unexpected, pulled willy nilly through magic gateways. I feel some empathy with old Sir John Dalyell, who in 1851 published the first description of *Cancerilla tubulata*, a copepod parasitic on brittle stars. It appeared in a volume entitled *The Powers of the Creator Displayed in the Creation* – clearly an author somewhat addicted to the miraculous.

With all this experience of the barely credible, I have sometimes wondered how I should have come to regard myself had I been a profoundly religious person. Holier than the pope? More reverent than an archbishop? More fanatical than an ayatollah? More single-minded than a Free Presbyterian? It's an intriguing, if somewhat frightening speculation.

In the middle of Sri Lanka, I remember an enormous recumbent Buddha. There he lies, arm comfortably crooked, hand supporting his head. Tranquil, benign, with a reassuring air of conserving energy. Now that's an atmosphere with which I think I could identify.

Send in the Clowns

A student finds his Wellingtons disappearing in the mud on a field trip at Strangford.

It would be a mistake to suppose that a career spent in biological research and teaching consists mainly of grim endeavour, the frustration of failed projects and dead ends and that question which often echoes down the years: "What the hell am I doing this for? Does it really make any significant difference to anyone?" It's true, of course, when all goes well and your animals are revealing some tiny new facet of their structure or behaviour, that you feel you are walking into a Metro-Goldwyn-Mayer sunset to the sound of a celestial choir. But every now and again the prevailing sound is laughter and the spectacle a farce. These are occasions to be cherished, when scientists, however dedicated, become eminently human. Biology is particularly prone to such healing moments because, quite often, life is a laugh.

When I was first exposed to zoological literature it included some Victorian and Edwardian snippets. I imagined the writers of this rather stilted prose as solemn and industrious scientists, sustained by a rigorous work ethic. When I had to participate in shore-collecting trips, their stoic images would float before me as I tried, in vain, to ignore the driving rain and freezing dawn winds of March on the shores of Strangford. My predecessors fifty years earlier would never, surely, have noticed the discomfort of frostbitten fingers and toes. It was much later, along less known literary byways, that the awful truth would sometimes leak out. As an example of backsliding in the line of duty, take the case of that splendid copepodologist George Brady who, in 1905, was invited to sample the fauna of a disused quarry, which was periodically flooded by salt water at high tide. His naturalist friend, Mr Meek, planned this expedition. Brady writes: "I was to have accompanied him, but was unable to do so owing to inclement weather and the necessity of rising earlier in the morning than I found quite agreeable". I couldn't have put it better myself.

The dedication and ingenuity of marine biologists a century ago led to some remarkable instances of seizing whatever opportunity might arise. Isaac Thompson and his companion W.S. McMillan took ship in the spring of 1887 to visit Madeira and the Canaries, hoping to obtain plankton samples en route. They even improvised a special plankton net which they could tow behind the ship. Let Isaac take up the tale: "… the speed of the vessel was too great to allow of any captures. The mails could not give way to the study of biology, so our genial captain would not allow any temporary stoppage; but the death of a poor fireman on the fourth day out necessitating a funeral pause of a few minutes, we took advantage of the opportunity by getting a haul …".

It is so easy to visualise this little drama. The description of the captain as 'genial' and the implied sympathy extended to the deceased 'poor fireman' acceptably cover a steely resolution to obtain their specimens at all costs. I wonder if they ever told the captain what was going on as the ship slowed for the committal.

Occasionally, public perception of animals will lead you into the realm of near-fantasy. One day, the phone rang in the Zoology Department and I picked it up. The caller was a native of Antrim, a town some twenty miles from Belfast. It seemed that an elderly badger had been shot the previous day and examination of the body had greatly puzzled my correspondent and his mates.

"Why was that?" I asked.

"Well" he said, "this badger only had one arse."

"How many did you expect?" I said, visualising a badger equipped with multi-exhausts like a powerful motorbike. There was a pause and then his tone became sceptical.

"I don't know what you folk in Belfast know about badgers, but it's well known here that for every year they live, they grow an extra arse." My motorbike analogy had not been so far out! The only explanation I could suggest was that, like many carnivores, badgers have glands around the anus. It may be that in some older individuals, these perianal openings become more obvious. However, I got the distinct impression that my caller regarded his conversation with me as a total waste of time.

Of course, it is not only the lay public who can latch on to the wrong idea. For some years, the Department purchased earthworms for dissection from Jimmy, who was a local bus conductor. He was a sleight of hand expert who would flip the correct change into your outstretched hand within half a second, no matter what coins you had proffered for your fare. His dexterity in catching earthworms was even greater. Jimmy's worms were invariably enormous, hinting at an amazingly favourable environment, but he resisted any attempt to disclose his source of supply. At that time, we happened to have an assistant lecturer who was an earthworm specialist. The only clue he managed to extract was Jimmy's remark that he always dug them at daybreak.

"Isn't it astonishing?" Alan confided. "Here we have a man, totally ignorant of biology, who has discovered a fundamental fact about earthworm ecology – that the biggest worms must migrate to the surface at dawn!" Concealing some scepticism, I tackled Jimmy in private.

"Why do you dig your worms at dawn, Jimmy?"

"Well, Doc," he said, "it's the only time I can get at the flower beds in the Botanic Gardens without being arrested by the park wardens."

Sometimes it is one's own lack of experience or imagination which becomes the source of a little humour, although its appreciation is generally retrospective – embarrassment comes first. Nearly twenty years ago, I was sent a small collection of parasitic copepods by a French research unit at Brest. This included a single specimen of a tiny crustacean, 1.6mm long, which had been taken in a plankton sample from a depth of 100 metres off the northwest African coast. Although it had been sent to me as an unidentified copepod, several features hinted that its affinities might lie instead with another crustacean group, the isopods – one of which, the woodlouse or slater of our gardens, will be familiar to the reader. However, despite a quick search through the relevant literature, no isopod family seemed to embrace this curious little animal, which rather resembled a grotesque gnome. Its most notable feature was a pair of very large, stout hind limbs, each terminating in a powerful grasping organ, uncannily similar to the ankle fetter of a bygone age. In a fever of uncertainty, I sent photos of my beast to three colleagues for their opinion. Like me, they had all seen bizarre copepods which had evolved in highly improbably ways and

A mystery crustacean, bearing "handcuffs" on its hind legs. Scale=1mm

agreed with my final decision to describe the animal as a copepod but not to assign it to any known family.

By this stage, I had even thought up a provisional scientific name for it – *Pedepodium paradoxum*, translatable as 'the strange fetter-footed one'. All was going well until Geoffrey Boxshall (British Museum of Natural History) came up with an idea of the crustacean's true relationship. On checking, it was immediately plain that he was right. What we were dealing with was, in fact, an isopod belonging to the family *Dajidae*, which are specialists in attaching themselves to other marine animals. Somehow, I had overlooked them completely. This was even more reprehensible, since I had learned that the animals taken in the same plankton haul were a species of krill – shrimp-like crustaceans which are a major item in the diet of the larger whales. Dajids are also associated with krill and the main use of the amazing look-alike fetter or handcuff on the last pair of legs is to lock on to the eyestalk of krill – another example of supreme adaptation. These isopods can grow relatively large, so my tiny example was clearly a juvenile and I eventually described it as such. In retrospect, it was a considerable relief not to have branded it as a copepod. Professionally speaking, that would have taken a lot of living down!

Hope springs eternal in the world of biology. A medical officer of health called one day at the Department and produced a photo of a large mysterious sea beast, which he had found, much decomposed, at Marblehill strand in County Donegal. The photo revealed little of diagnostic value, but the doctor insisted that a leg was present "I danced up and down on it, to make sure it was solid!" Intrigued, a colleague and I set forth the following day on a hundred mile drive to view this phenomenon. All rational arguments convinced us that a small whale was involved, but our medic's insistence on a 'leg' conjured up visions of what we would now call a Jurassic Park syndrome. Well, it was a whale. The 'leg' turned out to be a large and well-preserved penis, but at least I had a story which stood me in good stead for thirty years of extra-mural lecturing.

Most of the extra-mural work I did was for the Workers' Educational Association. These were rather challenging lectures, since a very wide age spectrum was involved and equally broad levels of intelligence and interest. It was a fairly good bet that some of the elderly clients would be significantly deaf, so one had to concentrate on getting them unobtrusively to the front of the group. I learned two aspects of technique very quickly. 1. Never patronise them as amateurs. 2. Give them as much up to date material as possible, providing it is spectacular. In the early fifties a lot of research was being carried out on bat sonar, for example and also on the biology of the deep ocean. I used to enjoy giving these 'Gee Whiz' lectures, but thankfully never quite plumbed the uttermost depths of banality by entitling a lecture 'Fish that Shine in the Dark'. One has to draw the line somewhere.

I have clear recollections of one such talk, which took place on a bitterly cold winter's night in Londonderry. Snow had been lying for some days and the appalling weather precluded the 80-mile journey by car. I stepped off the train in arctic conditions and eventually located the venue. It was a room in an old, bleak building, but some thoughtful organiser had built an enormous coal fire which was roaring away like a large incendiary bomb. Ten clients had braved the elements, none under sixty and several certainly a lot older. Naturally enough, they had retained their overcoats, scarves, gloves and hats.

With all windows firmly closed and the fire encouraged by still more coal, I started the proceedings. Five minutes passed and all my audience were bright-eyed and bushy-tailed. The heat in the room built up further and a few minutes later several pairs of glazed eyes were apparent. After twenty minutes, four of them, necks slumped, were clearly asleep. At the half hour, believe it or not, they were all unconscious. A professional hypnotist could not have done better. I persevered for another five minutes and then stopped. No one stirred. I picked up my gear and tiptoed out.

To forestall your questions: No, I was not invited back to Londonderry for any sort of repeat performance; and yes, I slept most of the way back to Belfast. The carriage was nearly as hot as the inferno I had just left.

The occasions when animals behave in totally unexpected ways have their place in biological humour. In my time I have been savaged by a variety of exotic invertebrates. These have included being stung by the notorious Portuguese man-of-war (a colonial relation of the jellyfish) and bitten by a giant centipede. The former was extremely painful, but was entirely my own fault, as I had deliberately let a tentacle of a very small specimen trail across my hand to see if the stinging cells of this little juvenile really packed a punch. They certainly did, but I recovered quickly. However, the worst attack I suffered gave me a real surprise.

I had taken a party of enthusiastic adults for a dredging trip in Strangford. On our final haul the dredge delivered a good collection of interesting animals, including a small northern octopus (*Eledone cirrosa*). I took it in my hand and demonstrated its main features to the fascinated group.

"Isn't it dangerous to handle?" someone said. "Surely it can bite?"

"Oh yes" I said airily, "but I've done this scores of times and never been bitten yet." At this precise moment, the little devil leaned forward, as if bowing in acquiescence to this rash boast and simultaneously sank its beak-like jaws into the skin between my thumb and forefinger. The shock to my nervous system was considerable, but the enveloping tentacles hid the actual deed from the spectators. As casually as I could, I shook the octopus into a bucket and pocketed my wounded hand, which began to throb and presently to swell. By the time we reached the quay, I was in a mild panic. My hand now resembled a moderate sized balloon and was really painful. In addition, I had fallen victim to the atavistic fears of childhood and remembered the folklore pertaining to cuts in that part of one's anatomy. Leafing frantically through a volume on marine toxins, I could hear grim-voiced prophecies from the remote past: "You'll get lockjaw, you know, even if it's treated at once!"

The literature, however, was reassuring. It confirmed my recollection that octopuses have no elaborate poison glands as such, but the secretion of their oral glands contain potent chemicals which have dramatic effects on their chief prey, crabs. I was evidently substituting for a large helping of crabmeat. The situation was complicated by the fact that I was supposed to travel to Scotland the following day to represent Ulster in a tennis fixture. I had a bad night, but by dawn the swelling had completely subsided and all was well. However, I have never since handled an octopus in the same cavalier fashion.

As I have said, this octopus behaved in a quite unexpected manner. Let me tell you of a much more spectacular example. Many years ago, an enormous dog periodically invaded our garden. It would appear shortly after dusk and pad delicately along the paths or lope gracefully across the lawn. It was an almost white Old English sheepdog and in the dim light it could have been mistaken for a Shetland pony. I have a soft spot for very large dogs and tried to encourage it. Although Gwyneth was by no means hostile to canines, the idea of so vast an animal using our laboriously nurtured flower beds as a convenience led to her disapproval of my attempts to establish rapport. So my affair with this big vagrant perforce went underground. In any case, the dog was so shy that any move on my part would send it retreating into the darkness.

Things remained at this impasse for weeks. Then something happened which altered the situation completely. I saw a new advertisement on television which extolled a male toilet product called Hai Karate. The half-minute plug showed a handsome young man arriving at his country cottage in his open sports car. He has already splashed a few drops of the magic potion about his person and is greeted by several gorgeous girlfriends who are clearly besotted with him. They cook for him, attend to his every whim and are devastated when he drives off in his macho car the following day. After being brainwashed by this for a few days, I announced, to no one in particular, that I would certainly welcome a bottle of this marvellous fluid. Shortly after, one mysteriously appeared and I experimentally anointed myself.

I can tell you now that it had absolutely no effect on any female of my acquaintance. But when my hitherto untouchable dog friend reappeared, the difference was quite incredible. Its extreme shyness was replaced by a boisterous playfulness of a sort which indicated that its hormones had been thoroughly stirred up. It materialised frequently (by day now, as well as night) and made gardening almost impossible, since I never heard it coming. Nostrils dilated and full of the joys of Spring, it would fondly embrace me. Once, on being thus ambushed from behind while mowing the lawn, I even considered slipping away unobtrusively to leave its great furry paws on the handle of the machine and so get my grass cut until the amorous impulse faded. When I had used up the bottle of aphrodisiac, the sex maniac left the garden and in fact I never saw him again. I did think of writing to the pharmaceutical firm to tell them that, in my experience, their product had no effect whatsoever on women – but if you were addicted to Old English sheepdogs, the stuff was pure dynamite.

As a biologist, I was once asked how I would explain the antics of mating dogs to a small, enquiring child. I forget what I said, but have sometimes wished I had the mental agility displayed by Noel Coward's aunt. When Noel was five, his favourite aunt would take him for walks in the area of St John's Wood. One day, on the opposite pavement, a pair of dogs, thus occupied, were proceeding slowly along, headed in the same direction. After gazing at them intently Noel tugged his aunt's hand. "What are those dogs doing, Auntie?" he asked. Instantaneously his aunt replied briskly "Well you see dear, the poor little doggie in front is blind and her kind friend is guiding her to St Dunstan's hospital"

FOOTPRINTS IN THE SEA

Nearly fifty years ago, an acquaintance was researching on mussels at the Port Erin marine station on the Isle of Man. Much of his work centred on analysing and comparing the currents of water entering and leaving the animal. Bivalves such as mussels behave rather like sea squirts as regards filtering. However, the inlet and outlet apertures, close together at the large, rounded end of the mussel shell, are only barely prolonged into siphonal tubes, which makes sampling the inhalant and exhalant water more difficult.

He quickly found that to envelop these openings with rigid material such as glass or plastic tubing, caused the mussel to suspend all filtering activities immediately. It took him some time to find the answer. The only type of tubing which the mussels would tolerate in close proximity to their siphons was very soft, very thin rubber. By this time, you may well be ahead of me and divined that large numbers of condoms became vital for his research. Furnished with these, suitably modified, the work proceeded smoothly.

It was at this point that he received a letter from Dublin to say that he had obtained a post with the Fisheries Department of the Irish Republic. Although his research was still unfinished, he realised that there was no shortage of mussels around the Irish coast, so there were no worries on that score. It was only on the day before he was due to leave that a paralysing thought struck him. His stock of condoms had run out – and condoms were banned in the Irish Republic. This embargo was, in fact, very strictly enforced, so he would have to bring a personal supply with him. Accordingly, he hurried to the nearest chemist.

"I need some condoms" he explained.

"Certainly sir" said the chemist, his voice dropping discreetly, "how many would you like?"

"Twelve dozen should be enough" said my friend, after a brief calculation. The chemist eyed him with some surprise and, possibly, a little envy.

"I'll just check if I have that number in stock" he said. A moment later he reappeared.

"I wonder, sir" he enquired "if ten dozen would do?"

"It'll have to" was the answer. "Just one other point, sir – would you like them with or without teats?"

"It doesn't really matter" he replied abstractedly. "You see, I always cut the ends off before I use them."

Send in the clowns? Don't bother – they're here.

Postscript

In the unlikely event of a reader becoming seriously addicted to some of the topics discussed in these chapters, I have added the following notes that will guide them to the original literature. Since parts of this are inevitably couched in somewhat obscure scientific jargon, its inclusion here merely reflects my own ingrained obsession that if you indulge in scientific research, of whatever sort, you should at least put your facts or speculations in the shop window.

Chapter 1: A general account of the biology of the female *Mychophilus roseus* (the "little red sausage") will be found in *On Mycophilus roseus Hesse and other notodelphyoid copepods from Strangford Lough, Co Down,* by R.V. Gotto. Published in the Proceedings of the Zoological Society of London, volume 124, part 3, pages 659-668 (1954). The structure and ecology of the male *Mychophilus* is given in *Description of the adult male Mychophilus roseus Hesse (Copepoda:Cyclopoida): A copepod with remarkable sensory equipment.* By R.V. Gotto, J.M.C. Holmes and R.P. Lowther. Published in Irish Naturalists' Journal, volume 21, part 7, pages 305-313 (1984).

Chapter 2: Accounts of the Armada, with specific reference to Spanish shipwrecks on the Irish coast, can be found in several small books by members of the Ulster Museum staff and are available in the Ulster Museum bookshop, Stranmillis Road, Belfast. These include descriptions of the treasure salvaged from the Girona, much of which (including the 'golden salamander') is on display. The story of the Girona wreck has also been written by its discoverer, Robert Stenuit, in his book *Treasures of the Armada* (1972), published by David and Charles, London.

Chapter 4: A brief summary of the Clunies Ross connection with the Cocos Keeling islands appeared in an article entitled *King of Cocos Islands finally loses his realm* by Peter Wombwell, which was published in the Daily Telegraph of August 25th 1988. Captain Joshua Slocum in his book *Sailing Alone Around the World* gives an enchanting glimpse of the atoll, where he spent a month in 1897. Although Slocum's book first appeared in Great Britain in 1900, a paperback edition was published in 1996 by Phoenix, London. Felix Wood Jones' paper *The Fauna of Cocos-Keeling Atoll* can be found in the Proceedings of the Zoological Society of London, pages 132-159 (1909). Charles Darwin's original work *On the Structure and Distribution of Coral Reefs* was printed in 1842.

Chapter 6: This chapter mentions associations of various sorts between different animal species. I wrote a short book on some marine examples for non-specialist biologists thirty years ago, entitled *Marine Animals: Partnerships and Other Associations*, published by English Universities Press (1969).

A detailed account by R.E. Elger (1969) of the ecology of the Jersey tiger moth in Rhodes, appeared in the German journal Oecologia, volume 2, no. 2, pages 162-197, entitled *Freilandstudien zur Biologie und Ökologie von Panaxia quadripunctaria (Lepidoptera, Arctiidae) auf der Insel Rhodos.* Do not let the German text put you off, since an excellent summary in English is included. Many colour photographs of Jersey tiger moths at Petaloudes illustrate a booklet entitled *The Butterflies of Rhodes* by Michael E. Arfaras, published by Kamiros Editions, Athens.

The production of light by the long-armed brittle star *Acrocnida brachiata* is recorded in a short paper entitled *Luminescent ophiuroids and associated copepods* by R.V. Gotto (1963). Irish Naturalists' Journal, volume 14, part 7, pages 137-139.

Chapter 8: The researches on which these examples are mainly based are described in the following papers (given in the order in which they occur in chapter 8).

Cocculinika – J.B. Jones and B.A. Marshall (1986). *Cocculinika myzorama, new genus, new species, a parasitic copepod from a deep-sea wood-ingesting limpet.* Journal of Crustacean Biology, volume 1, part 1, pages 166-169.

Ascidicola and *Corella* – Gotto, R.V. (1957). *The biology of a commensal copepod, Ascidicola rosea Thorell, in the ascidian Corella parallelogramma (Müller).* Journal of the Marine Biological Association U.K., volume 36, pages 281-290.

Sabelliphilus and *Sabella* – Gotto, R.V. (1960). *Observations on the orientation and feeding of the copepod Sabelliphilus elongates M. Sars on its fan-worm host.* Proceedings of the Zoological Society of London, volume 133, part 4, pages 619-628.

Eunicicola and *Eunice* – Gotto, R.V. (1963). *Observations on the structure, affinities and biology of a rare copepod Eunicicola (formerly Eurynotus) insolens (T. & A. Scott).* Proceedings of the Zoological Society of London, volume 140, part 1, pages 47-56.

Synaptiphilus and *Leptosynapta* – Gotto, R.V. (1984). *Observations on Synaptiphilus tridens (T. & A. Scott) an ectoassociate of holothurians.* Crustaceana (supplement 7) pages 214-216.

Notopterophorus – Gotto, R.V. and Threadgold, L.T. (1980). *Observations and speculations on the alate processes of the ascidicolous copepod Notopterophorus papilio (Cyclopoida: Notodelphyidae).* Journal of Zoology, London, volume 190, part 3, pages 337-363.

Pachypygus and its two types of male. – R. Hipeau-Jacquotte (1988). *Environmental Sex Determination in a Crustacean Parasite.* International Journal of Invertebrate Reproduction and Development. Volume 14, pages 11-24.

Chapter 9: The strange little crustacean, found in a plankton haul off northwest Africa, was described in the following paper: Gotto, R.V. (1983). *A hitherto undescribed juvenile stage of a female dajid isopod.* Journal of Crustacean Biology, volume 3, part 4, pages 629-635.

Dear Reader

I hope you have enjoyed this publication from Ballyhay Books. It is one of a growing number of local interest books published under this imprint including Hugh Robinson's *Back Across the Fields of Yesterday* and *The Book of 1000 Beautiful Things and Other Favourites* ; Aideen D'Arcy's *Lie Over Da* ; John O'Sullivan's *Belfast City Hospital, a Photographic History* and Harry Allen's *The Men of the Ards.*

To see details of these books as well as the beautifully illustrated books of our sister imprint, Cottage Publications, why not visit our website at **www.cottage-publications.com** or contact us at:–

Laurel Cottage
15 Ballyhay Rd
Donaghadee
Co. Down
N. Ireland
BT21 0NG

Tel: +44 (0)28 9188 8033

Timothy S Johnston

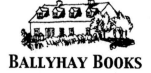

BALLYHAY BOOKS